zoom
Deutsch 2

Foundation Workbook

Oliver Gray

OXFORD

Great Clarendon Street, Oxford OX2 6DP

Oxford University Press is a department of the University of Oxford.

It furthers the University's objective of excellence in research, scholarship,
and education by publishing worldwide in
Oxford New York Auckland Cape Town Dar es Salaam Hong Kong Karachi
Kuala Lumpur Madrid Melbourne Mexico City Nairobi New Delhi Shanghai
Taipei Toronto

With offices in
Argentina Austria Brazil Chile Czech Republic France Greece Guatemala
Hungary Italy Japan South Korea Poland Portugal Singapore Switzerland
Thailand Turkey Ukraine Vietnam

Oxford is a registered trade mark of Oxford University Press in the UK and in certain
other countries

British Library Cataloguing in Publication Data

Data available

ISBN 978 019 912779 5

10 9 8 7 6 5 4 3 2

Printed in Great Britain by Ashford Colour Press Ltd, Gosport

Paper used in the production of this book is a natural, recyclable product made
from wood grown in sustainable forests. The manufacturing process conforms to the
environmental regulations of the country of origin.

Acknowledgements

The author and publisher would like to thank the following people for their help and
advice: Jenny Gwynne (editor), Angelika Libera (language consultant).

Audio recordings by Colette Thomson for Footstep Productions; Andrew Garratt (engineer)

The author and publisher would like to thank the following for their permission to
reproduce photographs and other copyright material:
p.12: Photodisc/OUP; **p.44**: Ingo Wagner/dpa/Corbis; **p.57**: elxeneize/iStock;
p.60: Jo Chambers/Shutterstock; Jo Chambers/Alamy

Illustrations by Matt Ward

Every effort has been made to contact copyright holders of material reproduced in this
book. If notified, the publishers will be pleased to rectify any errors or omissions at the
earliest opportunity.

Inhalt

Pronunciation

As you listen to the recordings for pages 4–7, repeat each word or phrase; imitate the pronunciation as closely as you can, to help you sound more German.

Consonants / Konsonanten

Many German consonants are pronounced the same way as in English. Listen to these examples.

b	**B**erlin
d	**D**ialog
f	**F**isch
h	**H**aus
k	**K**omödie
l	**l**ustig
m	**M**usical
n	**n**ein
p	**P**olen
t	**T**ischtennis

Fischer Fritz frisst frische Fische!

> **g** Remember: *g* is always 'hard' as in 'ground', 'gap'. One exception is the 'soft g' at the end of a word imported from French: *Garage*.

 g

Das **G**ras ist **g**rün.
Gert spielt **g**ern **G**itarre.
Mor**g**en **g**ehen wir in den **G**arten.

> **j** *j* is pronounced like the English '*y*'.

 j

Bist du in **J**apan? **J**a!
Jetzt esse ich **J**oghurt.

> **r** *r* is quite a distinctive sound in German and needs practising because no sound in English is quite like it.

 r

Rüdesheim liegt am **R**hein.
Regen, **R**egen, immer **R**egen.
B**r**ing mir einen K**r**imi.

> **s** *s* is pronounced in various ways:
> 1 – like an English '*z*'
> 2 – like the English '*sh*'
> 3 – like an English '*s*'.

 **s**

sieben

 **sp st**

Wir **sp**ielen Golf.
Der Lehrer ist **st**reng.

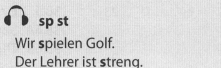 **s**

Wa**s** i**st** da**s**?
Du bi**st** lustig.

1 Listen to these words. What kind of s sound is there in each one? Label them 1, 2 or 3 to match the groups above.

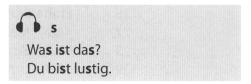 **s**

Sturm	☐	**s**ingen	☐
Sommer	☐	Ma**s**ke	☐
Skateboard	☐	**S**axofon	☐
streng	☐	fa**s**t	☐

> **ß** *ß* represents a double *s* when used after a <u>long</u> vowel.

 ß

Diese Stra**ß**e ist gro**ß**.
Wir lieben Fu**ß**ball.

Regen, Regen, immer Regen.

Pronunciation

 After a <u>short</u> vowel, *ss* is written instead. It sounds the same as *ß*.

 ss

Ich mu**ss** Schlu**ss** machen.
La**ss**t uns zum Schlo**ss** gehen.
Das ha**ss**e ich.

2 Try pronouncing these words correctly, then listen to check:

ss

küssen	blass	Bassgitarre
Spaß	Fuß	

 v is pronounced like the English 'f'.

v

Es gibt so **v**iel **V**erkehr.
Sebastian **V**ettel ist Rennfahrer.
Das ist **v**öllig **v**erboten.

 w is pronounced like the English 'v'.

w

Die Um**w**elt ist **w**ichtig.
Willst du **W**asserski fahren?
Wer **w**ohnt in dieser **W**ohnung?
Wir **w**ollen keine **W**olken sehen.

3 Try saying these sentences which contain *v* and *w*, and listen to check:

vw

Mein **V**ater hat einen **V**olkswagen.
Bremerha**v**en ist nicht **w**eit von **W**ilhelmsha**v**en.

 In German, *z* is very common. It is pronounced like the English 'ts'.

z

Die **Z**eit ist eine **Z**eitung.
In **Z**ürich gibt es einen **Z**oo.

Combinations of consonants

 The combination of *c* and *h* sounds similar to the *ch* at the end of the Scottish exclamation 'och!'

ch

A**ch**tung!
Bist du schon a**ch**tzehn?
La**ch**en ist gesund.
Ein Lo**ch** ist im Eimer.
Das ist e**ch**t super.

Lachen ist gesund.

 The same *ch* sound can also come at the end of a word ending in *-ig*:

ig

Du bist lust**ig**!
Heute ist es wolk**ig**.

 The *sh* sound is common in German and is spelt *sch*.

sch

Engli**sch** ist **sch**wierig aber Deut**sch** ist **sch**wieriger, sagt der **sch**lechte **Sch**üler!

VW

 Another common combination of consonants is *pf*:

pf

Ein **Pf**und **Pf**laumen, bitte.
Walter Tell hatte einen A**pf**el auf dem Ko**pf**.

 Finally, *zw*. Two sounds, like English 'ts' and 'v', are put together:

zw

Zwei ist **zw**ischen eins und drei.
Das Museum ist von **zw**ölf bis **zw**anzig Uhr geöffnet.

Pronunciation

Vowels / Vokale

| a | *a* can be pronounced as a long vowel or a short vowel. |

🎧 **long a / langes a**

Mein V**a**ter ist auf der Str**a**ße.
Wir b**a**den jeden T**a**g.
M**a**len bringt Sp**a**ß.

🎧 **short a / kurzes a**

L**a**sst uns für F**a**sching einen Kuchen b**a**cken.
W**a**s m**a**cht der M**a**nn?
Es ist f**a**st **a**cht.

In English, *a* is a very open sound, as in the English word 'cat'. In German, *a* is almost like an English *u*, as in the English 'cut'. Listen to these words to hear the difference.

🎧

English: h**a**t   English: c**a**t
German: h**a**t   German: K**a**tze

However, when German adapts an English word, the *a* sounds more like an English *e*.

🎧 H**a**ndy

| e | In German, the short *e* is pronounced like the English *e* in 'elephant'. It is never pronounced like the other English *e* as in 'me'. |

🎧 **short e / kurzes e**

T**e**nnis ist h**e**ktisch.
Fr**e**ddie ist fr**e**ch.
England ist ein n**e**ttes Land.

There is also a long **e**, as underlined here:

🎧 **long e / langes e**

Eva hat einen **E**sel.
Ich habe noch nie in meinem L**e**ben einen **E**lefanten ges**e**hen.

4 Listen to these words. What kind of *e* sound is there? Write S for short, L for long.

🎧 e

W**e**sten	☐	d**e**n	☐
g**e**hen	☐	d**e**nn	☐
T**e**st	☐	w**e**nn	☐
kl**e**ben	☐	W**e**h	☐

| i | *i* is always pronounced short, as in the English 'in'. |

🎧 i

Ich finde S**i**lvester toll.
Ich b**i**n **i**n einem **I**nternetcafé.
K**i**nder s**i**nd n**i**cht b**i**llig.

| o | *o* can be short or long. The short *o* is pronounced |

like this:

🎧 **short o / kurzes o**

Mein C**o**mputer ist t**o**ll.
Oliver mag **O**liven.
Ich esse **o**ft P**o**mmes.

The long *o* is pronounced like this:

🎧 **long o / langes o**
Ostermontag
B**o**chum ist eine Großstadt.
Wir w**o**hnen an der D**o**nau.

5 Listen: what kind of *o* sound does each word have? Write S for short, L for long.

🎧

H**o**se	☐	Kr**o**nberg	☐
B**o**ss	☐	**O**pa	☐
v**o**ll	☐	B**o**nn	☐
D**o**se	☐		

Pronunciation

 u can be short or long. The short *u* is pronounced like this:

 short u / kurzes u

Unsere **U**mwelt m**u**ss nicht schm**u**tzig sein.
Uschi ist l**u**stig.

The long *u* is pronounced like this:

 long u / langes u

Wir machen M**u**sik in der Sch**u**le.
Hast d**u** mein B**u**ch?
Mein H**u**t, der hat drei Ecken.

6 Listen: what kind of *u* sound does each word have? Write S for short, L for long.

Z**u**g	☐	F**u**ß	☐
m**u**tig	☐	t**u**t	☐
unfreundlich	☐	K**u**ss	☐

Combinations of vowels

 ie is pronounced as in the English word 'keep'.

 ie

Trink nicht zu v**ie**l B**ie**r.
Ich l**ie**be T**ie**re.
Wir v**ie**r sind h**ie**r.

ei is pronounced as in the English word 'eye'.

ei

Wie h**ei**ßt du?
M**ei**n Name ist H**ei**di.
M**ei**ne Stadt ist k**ei**ne Kl**ei**nstadt.

7 Read these words out loud, then listen to check:

 ie / ei

viel	Siemens	Ziel
dein	Bein	Biene
Brief	seit	

 au is pronounced as in the English word 'cow'.

au

Ich mache H**au**s**au**fgaben zu H**au**se – natürlich!
Meine bl**au**e Hose ist s**au**ber.

Umlauts

An umlaut is a little symbol that changes the sound of an *a*, *o* or *u*. Listen to the difference the umlaut makes.

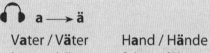 **a ⟶ ä**

V**a**ter / V**ä**ter	H**a**nd / H**ä**nde
h**a**tte / h**ä**tte	f**a**hre / f**ä**hrt

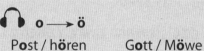 **o ⟶ ö**

P**o**st / h**ö**ren	G**o**tt / M**ö**we
r**o**t / L**ö**we	

Ich liebe Tiere.

u ⟶ ü

m**u**ss / m**ü**ssen	m**u**sste / K**ü**ste
Gr**u**ß / gr**ü**ßen	fünf**u**ndf**ü**nfzig
p**u**r / T**ü**r	

8 Listen to ten words. Can you identify which ones contain an umlaut? Here are the main vowels in these words: add an umlaut if you think it is necessary:

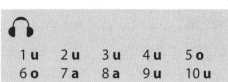

1 **u**	2 **u**	3 **u**	4 **u**	5 **o**
6 **o**	7 **a**	8 **a**	9 **u**	10 **u**

1 **Read about these two people. Draw pictures to show what they look like.**

> Meine Freundin Vanessa hat braune Augen und lange braune lockige Haare. Sie trägt keine Brille, aber manchmal trägt sie Ohrringe. Ich finde Vanessa toll!

Vanessa

> Mein Freund Peter hat blaue Augen und er trägt eine Brille. Er trägt auch einen Ohrring. Er hat kurze glatte Haare. Peter ist sehr cool!

Peter

2 🎧 **Listen to this girl describing herself. Circle the correct words in the sentences.**

a Sylvia has <u>blonde</u> / <u>brown</u> hair.

b Her hair is <u>quite long</u> / <u>very long</u>.

c She wears <u>glasses</u> / <u>no glasses</u> and <u>always</u> / <u>often</u> wears earrings.

d Her hair is <u>straight</u> / <u>curly</u>.

3 **Choose one girl and one boy in your class. Write a brief description in German of each one (hair, eyes, etc.). Pass your description to a partner. Can your partner work out who you are describing?**

_____

_____

_____

_____

_____

0.2 Wie bist du?

1 Find ten words describing character in this wordsearch. They can be across, down or diagonal.

arrogant
gemein
frech
sympathisch
schüchtern
lustig
unfreundlich
nervig
launisch
nett

A	I	ß	C	Ö	F	P	C	I	G	O	H
W	S	Y	M	P	A	T	H	I	S	C	H
B	K	A	H	N	T	U	H	L	I	O	S
S	E	G	Ü	E	Ö	B	Ü	L	K	D	C
H	A	M	N	N	L	R	D	U	B	Z	H
P	R	W	D	Z	A	N	Z	S	C	S	Ü
ß	R	G	Ö	J	U	N	A	T	M	F	C
B	O	Ü	F	E	N	E	K	I	E	ß	H
W	G	I	R	Ö	I	R	F	G	A	J	T
M	A	F	E	A	S	V	Z	D	E	R	E
N	N	L	C	U	C	I	E	J	Z	F	R
U	T	G	H	B	H	G	E	M	E	I	N

2 🎧 Listen to six comments about people. Put a tick if the comment is positive and a cross if it is negative.

1 __X__   4 _____

2 _____   5 _____

3 _____   6 _____

3 Unjumble the <u>second half</u> of each sentence.

a Ich mag Mehmet, **ist er weil freundlich**

_____

b Ich mag Yesim nicht, **sie ist weil gemein**

_____

c Ich mag Doris, **sie ist sympathisch weil**

_____

0.3 Zu Hause

1 **Draw lines to link the pictures to the matching sentences.**

1

2

3

4

5

6

a Ich kaufe im Supermarkt ein.

b Ich wasche ab.

c Ich füttere die Katze.

d Ich decke den Tisch.

e Ich räume mein Zimmer auf.

f Ich sauge Staub.

2 **Choose a German adjective from the box to describe each of these people. Write it next to the sentence.**

a A dad who plays music from his youth. _____

b A mum who won't let her child play outside. _____

c A parent who gets annoyed if someone is late. _____

d Parents who have cool phones. _____

e A mum who doesn't mind if her children are out late. _____

> tolerant
> altmodisch
> ungeduldig
> streng
> modern

3 🎧 **Listen and find out which of the parents in Activity 2 is being described each time. Note the letter from Activity 2 for each one.**

1 ____d____   4 _____

2 _____   5 _____

3 _____

1 **Read these sentences. After each, write whether it is <u>present</u> or <u>perfect</u> tense.**

a Ich bin nach Dortmund gefahren. _____perfect_____

b Hassan hat einen Blog geschrieben. _____

c Lara schreibt einen Blog. _____

d Hast du ein Handy gekauft? _____

e Ben tanzt gern. _____

f Was machst du? _____

g Ich kaufe oft Bonbons. _____

h Ich habe ein Interview gemacht. _____

2 🎧 **Listen to someone talking about a day out. What order did he do things in? Number the phrases 1–7.**

caught bus ☐

walked into town
1️⃣

bought ticket ☐

went to restaurant ☐

went home ☐

ate pizza ☐

danced ☐

3 **Put the appropriate past participle into these sentences:**

a Ich habe eine neuen Computer _____.

b Er ist zu Fuß nach Hause _____.

c Ich habe ein Buch _____.

d Sie hat einen Brief _____.

e Du bist nach Nienburg _____.

geschrieben

gegangen

gelesen

gekauft

gefahren

1 Look at these mixed-up words. Each one could be used to describe somone's character. Write them out correctly.

a **rcnflduieh** _____

b **retnsg** _____

c **uelnduigdg** _____

d **rotnaarg** _____

e **scilprtoh** _____

f **megine** _____

2 🎧 Listen to Samira. What did she do yesterday? Put a tick or a cross by each sentence.

a She fed the dog. ☐

b She cleaned her bike. ☐

c She washed up. ☐

d She stayed in bed. ☐

e She did her maths homework. ☐

f She went into town. ☐

g She cleaned the bathroom. ☐

h She tidied her bedroom. ☐

3 Complete the sentences by writing *bin*, *sind*, *habe* or *haben* into the gaps.

a Wir _____ ein Auto gekauft.

b Ich _____ nach Berlin gefahren.

c Ich _____ das Badezimmer aufgeräumt.

d Wir _____ in die Disco gegangen.

Remember:

fahren and *gehen* use *sein* to form the perfect tense.

0.6A Sprachlabor

1 **Tick all the sentences which have the correct word order. Cross the others out.**

a Herr Meyer ist streng, aber er auch nett ist. ☐

b Ich mag Lars, weil er ist lustig. ☐

c Ich mag Claudia nicht, weil sie arrogant ist. ☐

d Ich putze das Badezimmer und ich räume auf. ☐

e Ich mag Ulla, weil sie hat blonde Haare. ☐

f Wir haben Pizza gemacht, weil wir Hunger haben. ☐

> *weil* (because) is a linking word which changes the word order. It sends the verb to the end:
> Ich mag Sira. Sie **ist** lustig.
> → Ich mag Sira, **weil** sie lustig **ist**.
>
> Other linking words such as *und* and *aber* don't change the word order:
> Ich mag Sira und sie ist lustig.

2 **Write out the three crossed-out sentences correctly.**

_____

_____

_____

> **The perfect tense with *haben* and *sein***
> Most verbs form their perfect tense with *haben*, and their past participles start with *ge-* and end with *-t*:
> Ich **habe** Fußball **ge**spiel**t**.
>
> A few verbs (mostly verbs of movement) use *sein* instead of *haben* to form the perfect tense. Most of their past participles start with *ge-* but end with *-en*:
> Ich **bin** in die Disco **ge**gang**en**.

3 **Fill the gaps using the correct words from the box below.**

a Ich ____habe____ eine CD ____gekauft____. (*bought*)

b Wir _____ ins Restaurant _____. (*went*)

c Du _____ eine E-Mail _____. (*wrote*)

d Hassan _____ Fußball _____. (*played*)

e Wir _____ nach Spanien _____. (*travelled*)

f Ich _____ das Praktikum _____. (*got*)

> sind   sind   habe   habe   hast   gespielt   geschrieben
> hat   bekommen   gegangen   gekauft   gefahren

die Super-Jungs

Wie sind die Super-Jungs wirklich? Wir haben sie gefragt.

Kai

Kai:
Ich tanze gut und ich singe auch gut. Was, arrogant, ich? Naja, okay, ich bin ein bisschen arrogant, aber ich bin auch sehr freundlich.

Marek

Marek:
Ich bin absolut nicht arrogant! Alle Mädchen mögen mich, weil ich schöne Haare und braune Augen habe. Ich bin manchmal launisch, aber nie gemein.

Omar

Omar:
Ich habe lockige Haare und trage einen Ohrring. Die Mädchen sagen, ich bin der Beste in der Band, weil ich so nett und auch sympathisch bin.

Phillipp

Phillipp:
Ich bin schüchtern, aber manchmal auch ein bisschen frech. Ich bin beliebt, weil ich nie unfreundlich bin.

1 **Read the magazine article and answer the questions below.**

a Underline all the adjectives in the interview.

b Double underline all the adjectives which come before a noun and therefore have an ending.

c Find one adjective exactly the same as in English and three that are similar to English.

The same: _____

Similar: _____ _____ _____

d Which adjectives, in your opinion, are difficult to guess because they are completely unlike English words?

_____

e Have an intelligent guess at what *beliebt* means. _____

f Why is *sympathisch* a false friend?

_____

0 Vokabular

Wie siehst du aus? / *What do you look like?*

Wie sieht er/sie aus?	*What does he/she look like?*
Ich habe/Er hat/Sie hat …	*I have/He has/She has …*
blaue/braune/grüne Augen.	*blue/brown/green eyes.*
blonde/braune/rote/ schwarze Haare.	*blonde/brown/red/black hair.*
lange/kurze/lockige/ glatte Haare.	*long/short/curly/straight hair.*
Trägst du …? Trägt er/sie …?	*Do you wear …? Does he/she wear …?*
Ich trage/Er trägt/Sie trägt … eine Brille/einen Ohrring.	*I wear/He wears/She wears … glasses/an earring.*
Ich trage keine Brille/keinen Ohrring.	*I don't wear glasses/an earring.*

Wie bist du? / *What's your character like?*

Ich bin/Er ist/Sie ist …	*I am/He is/She is …*
arrogant	*arrogant*
frech	*naughty*
freundlich	*friendly*
gemein	*mean*
launisch	*moody*
lustig	*funny*
nervig	*irritating*
nett	*nice*
schüchtern	*shy*
sympathisch	*nice*
unfreundlich	*unfriendly*
immer	*always*
manchmal	*sometimes*
nicht	*not*
nie	*never*
oft	*often*
sehr	*very*
selten	*rarely, seldom*
ziemlich	*quite*
Ich mag …, weil er/sie (nicht) … ist.	*I like … because he/she is (isn't) …*

Zu Hause / *At home*

Meine Eltern sind …	*My parents are …*
Mein(e) Vater/Mutter ist …	*My father/mother is …*
altmodisch	*old-fashioned*
lieb	*gentle, sweet, lovely*
modern	*modern*
streng	*strict*
tolerant	*tolerant*
ungeduldig	*impatient*
Wir verstehen uns (nicht) gut.	*We (don't) get on well.*
Das finde ich (nicht) … gut/schlecht/gemein.	*I (don't) think that's … good/bad/mean.*

Was machst du zu Hause? / *How do you help at home?*

Ich decke den Tisch.	*I set the table.*
Ich wasche ab.	*I do the washing-up.*
Ich putze das Badezimmer.	*I clean the bathroom.*
Ich füttere die Katze.	*I feed the cat.*
Ich sauge Staub.	*I do the vacuuming.*
Ich kaufe im Supermarkt ein.	*I go shopping in the supermarket.*
Ich räume mein Zimmer auf.	*I tidy my room.*
Wie oft machst du das?	*How often do you do that?*
jeden Tag	*every day*
einmal pro Woche	*once a week*

Warum bist du in Köln? / *Why are you in Cologne?*

Was hast du gemacht?	*What did you do?*
Ich habe/Du hast/Er/Sie hat	*I/You/He/She …*
Pizza/einen Test gemacht.	*made pizza/did a test.*
ein Ticket/eine CD gekauft.	*bought a ticket/CD.*
in der Disco getanzt.	*danced in the disco.*
eine Anzeige/ ein Buch gelesen.	*read an advert/book.*
eine E-Mail/einen Brief geschrieben.	*wrote an email/a letter.*
das Praktikum bekommen.	*got the work experience*
Ich bin/Du bist/Er ist/Sie ist …	*I/You/He/She …*
nach Zürich gefahren.	*went to Zurich.*
in die Stadt/in den Park gegangen.	*went into town/to the park.*

Checklist

How well do you think you can do the following?			
Write a sentence for each one if you can.			
	I can do this well	**I can do this but not very well**	**I can't do this yet**
1. describe my own and other people's appearance and personality			
2. say what I do to help at home			
3. talk about what I've done recently			
4. use the linking word *weil*			
5. use the perfect tense			
6. use different strategies to learn new words			

1A.1 Mein Alltag

1 Write in the times. Find the missing time (in tinted boxes down).

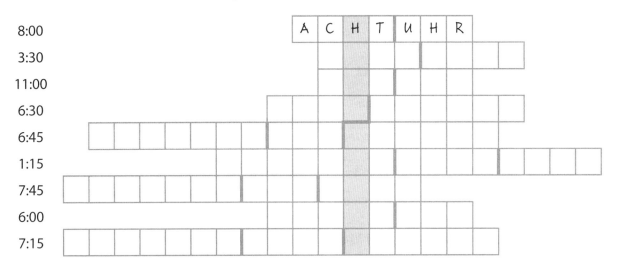

8:00	A C H T U H R
3:30	
11:00	
6:30	
6:45	
1:15	
7:45	
6:00	
7:15	

Missing time: _____

2 Draw lines to link the pictures to the matching sentences.

1

a Ich stehe auf.

2

b Ich gehe ins Bett.

3

c Ich fahre nach Hause.

4

d Ich wache auf.

5

e Ich frühstücke.

6

f Ich putze meine Zähne.

1 **Write out these jumbled perfect tense sentences correctly.**

a Wir gefrühstückt haben acht um Uhr

_Wir haben um ..._____

b Hannover Alex gefahren ist nach

_____

c telefoniert Ich mit habe Mama

_____

d Astrid gekocht Kaffee hat

_____

e gegessen hast Du Bratwurst eine

_____

f bin gegangen Ich Uhr zehn Bett um ins

_____

2 🎧 **Listen and decide in which order Almut did these things. Number the pictures 1–7 to show the order.**

a

b

c

d

e

f

g

1 🎧 Listen and write in figures the times being given by the radio announcer.

1 _11.15_ 3 _____ 5 _____ 7 _____

2 _____ 4 _____ 6 _____ 8 _____

2 Write out these word snakes correctly.

a IchhabemitmeinemBrudertelefoniert.

_____

b Wirhabenumhalbsiebenferngesehen.

_____

c Ulihatumhalbzweiabgewaschen.

_____

d IchhabedieKatzenichtgefüttert.

_____

e LeohatheuteMorgenradioZoomgehört.

_____

f HastdudeineE-mailsgecheckt?

_____

3 Read these times out loud to your partner.

a

Es ist zweiundzwanzig Uhr fünfundzwanzig.

b

c  d  e  f

1 🎧 **Listen to four people describing something they have done. Fill in the table in English.**

Name	Did what?	When?	Thought it was …
1 Ahmed			
2 Nina			
3 Kathi			
4 Max			

2 **These opinion words are all written backwards. Sort them out.**

a TTEN   *nett* ☐

b MMILHCS _____ ☐

c REPUS _____ ☐

d TUG _____ ☐

e TUAL _____ ☐

f THCELHCS _____ ☐

g TNASSERETNI _____ ☐

h HCSIDOMTLA _____ ☐

i GISSERTS _____ ☐

j LOOC _____ ☐

3 **When you have written out the words in Activity 2, put a cross by negative adjectives and a tick by positive ones.**

1A.5 Letztes Wochenende

1 **Add the missing parts to complete the past participles.**

a Fußball ge_____

b in die Disco ge_____

c im Schwimmbad ge_____

d nach Paris ge_____

e eine neue Hose ge_____

f Fotos ge_____

...schwommen
...gangen
...macht
...spielt
...fahren
...kauft

2 **Now write out full sentences using the phrases in Activity 1, starting Ich bin ... or Ich habe ...**

a Ich habe Fußball gespielt.

b _____

c _____

d _____

e _____

f _____

3 **Using vocabulary from the box on the right, answer these questions for yourself. (The answers don't have to be true!)**

Ich habe ... gegessen / gespielt / gemacht / besucht

Ich bin ... gegangen / gefahren

a Was hast du am Wochenende gemacht?

_____

_____

b Was hast du am Samstag gemacht?

_____

_____

c Was hast du am Sonntag gemacht?

_____

_____

1A.6A Sprachlabor

Separable and reflexive verbs

The infinitive of some German verbs needs to be split into two parts when used in the present tense. These are called **separable** verbs: **abwaschen** – Ich **wasche ab**. (*I wash up.*)

In the perfect tense, the prefix stays at the front of the verb, before **ge-**: Ich habe **abgewaschen**. (*I washed up.*)

With other German verbs, called **reflexive** verbs, you need to use an extra pronoun. The pronoun that goes with *ich* is *mich* (myself): sich setzen – Ich setze **mich** auf den Stuhl. (*I sit down on the chair.*)

A few verbs are both separable and reflexive: sich anziehen – Ich ziehe **mich an**. (*I get dressed.*)

1   **Which of these sentences contains a <u>reflexive</u> verb? Put a tick by those which do.**

a	Ich ziehe mich an.	✓ ☐	**f**	Ich ziehe mich aus.	☐ ☐
b	Ich wasche ab.	☐ ☐	**g**	Ich sehe fern.	☐ ☐
c	Ich gehe ins Bett.	☐ ☐	**h**	Ich räume auf.	☐ ☐
d	Ich frühstücke.	☐ ☐	**i**	Ich stehe auf.	☐ ☐
e	Ich wasche mich.	☐ ☐	**j**	Ich kaufe ein.	☐ ☐

2   **Put a cross by each sentence in Activity 1 with a <u>separable</u> verb.**

3   **Put the right prefix into these perfect tense sentences.**

a   Ich habe _____fern_____ gesehen. (*watched TV*)

b   Ich habe _____ gewaschen. (*washed up*)

c   Ich habe _____ geräumt. (*cleared up*)

d   Ich habe _____ gekauft. (*went shopping*)

e   Ich bin _____ gestanden. (*got up*)

Understanding times

1 🎧 **Listen and write down the time when Erwin did each action shown in the pictures.**

a  7.00

b

c

d

e

f

Reading for detail

2 **Read about Simone's weekend, then write out sentences a–f, correcting the mistakes.**

> Hallo! Ich heiße Simone. Das Wochenende war toll!
> Ich bin am Samstag mit meiner Schwester nach München gefahren. Wir haben in einem China-Restaurant gegessen, das war lecker. Am Nachmittag haben wir bei H&M Kleider gekauft. Ich habe ein T-Shirt gekauft und Monika hat eine schöne Jacke gekauft. Wir sind um 18 Uhr mit dem Bus nach Hause gefahren. Am Sonntag waren wir sportlich. Wir haben im Garten Tennis gespielt – drei Stunden lang! Wir waren ganz schön kaputt!

a Simone went to Munich on her own.

_____

b She didn't have any lunch.

_____

c She went shopping in the morning.

_____

d The shopping trip was unsuccessful.

_____

e She went home on foot.

_____

f On Sunday she lazed around.

_____

1A Vokabular

Mein Alltag	***My daily routine***
Ich wache auf.	*I wake up.*
Ich stehe auf.	*I get up.*
Ich wasche mich.	*I have a wash.*
Ich putze meine Zähne.	*I brush my teeth.*
Ich ziehe mich an.	*I get dressed.*
Ich frühstücke.	*I have breakfast.*
Ich fahre zur Arbeit.	*I go to work.*
Ich fahre nach Hause.	*I go home.*
Ich ziehe mich aus.	*I get undressed.*
Ich gehe ins Bett.	*I go to bed.*

Wie spät ist es?	***What time is it?***
Es ist Viertel vor acht.	*It's quarter to eight.*
Es ist acht Uhr.	*It's eight o'clock.*
Es ist Viertel nach acht.	*It's quarter past eight.*
Es ist halb neun.	*It's half past eight.*

Was hast du gemacht?	***What did you do?***
Was hast du gestern gemacht?	*What did you do yesterday?*
Ich habe …	*I …*
CDs gekauft.	*bought CDs.*
E-Mails gelesen.	*read emails.*
Fußball gespielt.	*played football.*
Hausaufgaben gemacht.	*did homework.*
Kaffee gekocht.	*made coffee.*
Musik gehört.	*listened to music.*
eine Nachricht geschrieben.	*wrote a message.*
Pizza gegessen.	*ate pizza.*
getanzt.	*danced.*
telefoniert.	*talked on the phone.*
Ich bin …	*I …*
ins Kino gegangen.	*went to the cinema.*
in die Stadt gefahren.	*went into town.*

Und gestern Abend …?	***And yesterday evening …?***
Es ist …/Um …	*It is …/At …*
neunzehn Uhr fünfunddreißig	*19.35*
siebzehn Uhr zwanzig	*17.20*
achtzehn Uhr zehn	*18.10*
zwanzig Uhr fünf	*20.05*
dreizehn Uhr fünfundfünfzig	*13.55*
Ich habe …	*I …*
aufgeräumt.	*tidied up.*
abgewaschen.	*did the washing-up.*
ferngesehen.	*watched TV.*

Es war super!	***It was great!***
Es/Das Konzert war …	*It/The concert was …*
Die Arbeit/Die Woche war …	*Work/The week was …*
anstrengend	*tiring, exhausting*
gut	*good*

interessant	*interesting*
langweilig	*boring*
laut	*loud, noisy*
nett	*nice*
schlecht	*bad*
schlimm	*awful*
schwer	*difficult, hard*
stressig	*stressful*
super	*super, great*
toll	*great*

Letztes Wochenende	***Last weekend***
Ich habe …	*I …*
Fotos geschickt.	*sent photos.*
Freunde getroffen/besucht.	*met/visited friends.*
ein Konzert besucht.	*went to a concert.*
gearbeitet.	*worked.*
gechattet.	*chatted.*
gegessen/getrunken.	*ate/drank …*
gewohnt.	*stayed/lived …*
mich entspannt.	*relaxed.*
Ich bin geschwommen.	*I swam.*

Checklist

How well do you think you can do the following?			
Write a sentence for each one if you can.			
	I can do this well	I can do this but not very well	I can't do this yet
1. describe my daily routine			
2. tell the time			
3. describe what I've done recently and give my opinion			
4. use reflexive and separable verbs			
5. use the perfect tense with *haben* and *sein*			
6. use the imperfect tense (*Es war …*)			

1B.1 Feiertage und Feste

1 Solve the clues and write the words in the grid. What is the missing festival (in the tinted box down)?

1 Flames (on a German river)

2 Unity Day (part 1)

3 A new year begins

4 Unity Day (part 2)

5 A festive date in December

6 Unity Day (part 3)

7 Good for bunnies!

8 Presents today in Germany

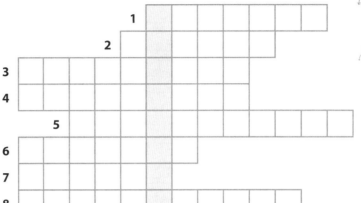

Missing festival: _____

2 Draw lines to link the dates with the matching words.

1/1	am neunundzwanzigsten Januar
2/1	am siebzehnten Januar
3/1	am vierten Januar
4/1	am dreiundzwanzigsten Januar
7/1	am dritten Januar
14/1	am vierzehnten Januar
17/1	am siebten Januar
20/1	am ersten Januar
23/1	am zweiten Januar
29/1	am zwanzigsten Januar

1 **Fill the gaps in these sentences. The English words in brackets tell you which verbs to use. (The words in the box can be used more than once.)**

a Ich _____kann_____ gut Tennis _____spielen_____ . *(can play)*

b Wir _____ um 22 Uhr ins Bett _____ . *(must go)*

c Wir _____ Hausaufgaben _____ . *(must do)*

d Paul _____ gut _____ . *(can sing)*

e Bettina _____ eine Party _____ . *(must organise)*

f Ich _____ nicht _____ . *(can't come)*

g Wir _____ Spaß _____ . *(can have)*

h Berni _____ . *(must wash up)*

muss	kann	können	müssen
abwaschen	gehen	haben	organisieren
machen	kommen	spielen	singen

2 🎧 **Listen and note down either __can__ or __must__, plus the activity (in English).**

1 _____can_____ _____go to town_____ .

2 _____ _____ .

3 _____ _____ .

4 _____ _____ .

5 _____ _____ .

6 _____ _____ .

7 _____ _____ .

8 _____ _____ .

1 Underline all the <u>modal verbs</u> in the text. Then write them out, in English, in the order in which they appear.

_____

> Leo: Letztes Jahr hat Sira eine Faschingsparty organisiert. Das war toll. Dieses Jahr <u>muss</u> ich die Party organisieren. Das ist aber schwer! Ich soll alles einkaufen. Das ist ein Problem, weil ich kein Geld habe. Wir wollen Karaoke singen, aber ich kann nicht singen. Ich will im Wohnzimmer feiern, aber meine Tante sagt, das darf ich nicht. Sie sagt auch, wir dürfen nicht trinken, nicht rauchen und nicht laut sein. Das wollen wir natürlich nicht! Und am nächsten Morgen muss ich alles aufräumen. Weißt du was? Ich organisiere keine Party!

2 Read Leo's text again and answer these questions.

a What's Leo's problem with shopping? _____

b And what's his problem with karaoke? _____

c Why can't they have the party in the living room? _____

d What aren't they allowed to do? _____

e What does Leo say about that? _____

f What would he have to do the next day? _____

g What conclusion does he reach? _____

3 Unjumble these sentences. Both are replies to invitations.

a Ja, gern. für Vielen Einladung die Dank.

_____

b Nein, ich leider kommen kann nicht.

_____

1B.4 Die Party war spitze!

1 🎧 **Listen to a description of a disastrous party. Choose the correct words to complete each statement.**

a The party was great / not bad / (terrible.)

b Lots of people / A few people / Nobody came.

c They ate and sang / danced and played games / ate and danced.

d It was fun / boring / exciting.

e The music was old-fashioned / loud / cool.

f Olli cooked / fell over / played music.

g He broke a cup / a table / a chair.

h Then he went home / was sick / fell asleep.

2 **Here's a description of a better party. Fill in the gaps with words from the box.**

a Die Party _____ spitze.

b Wir haben Einladungen _____ .

c Sandra hat Kuchen _____ .

d Hakan hat Musik _____ .

e Wir haben 50 Gäste _____ .

f Es _____ viel zu essen und zu trinken.

g Wir _____ alle viel Spaß.

h Ich _____ eine tolle Party machen und die Party

_____ auch toll!

wollte	hatten	eingeladen	geschrieben
war	war	gebacken	gab	gespielt

3 **How many of the words in the box above are past participles? Which words are they?**

_____

1B.5 Alle Jahre wieder

1 *Dezemberquiz.* **Find the ten December festival words in this grid.**

K	U	C	H	E	N	C	Ü	A	E	N	H
R	G	S	S	T	I	E	F	E	L	K	E
N	E	I	ß	I	K	E	R	O	E	N	I
A	M	L	G	M	O	Z	Ö	B	ß	U	L
Z	D	V	A	U	L	C	I	A	D	G	I
F	E	E	T	H	A	W	J	U	Ö	L	G
O	Z	S	E	Z	U	F	T	M	V	F	A
A	E	T	G	E	S	C	H	E	N	K	B
L	M	E	A	K	W	C	W	G	I	O	E
I	B	R	Ö	E	B	ß	G	K	A	Ü	N
W	E	I	H	N	A	C	H	T	E	N	D
L	R	T	C	F	H	E	N	A	D	K	S

Weihnachten
Geschenk
Dezember
Nikolaus
Gans
Baum
Silvester
Kuchen
Heiligabend
Stiefel

2 **Fill in the right question words.**

a _____ Geschenke hast du bekommen? – Zehn!

b _____ essen wir heute? – Gans.

c _____ ist der Kuchen? – Auf dem Tisch.

d _____ hat das Essen gekocht? – Mein Vater.

e _____ öffnen wir die Geschenke? – Um 18 Uhr.

f _____ kommen wir nach Hause? – Mit dem Auto.

> Wie   Wer   Wann   Was   Wie viele   Wo

Modal verbs

Modal verbs (*können, müssen, dürfen, wollen, sollen*) are used for saying what you **can**, **must**, **are allowed to**, **want to** or **should** do.

A modal verb is always the second idea in a German sentence. It is usually followed by an infinitive at the end of the sentence. For more details, see page 46 of your Student Book.

1 **Fill in the gaps with modal verbs from the box, to match the English words in brackets. (You can use the verbs more than once.)**

a Ich __will__ zur Party gehen, aber ich _____ es nicht. (*want, am allowed*)

b Wir _____ nicht abwaschen, aber wir _____ es tun. (*want, must*)

c Olli _____ gut in Mathe sein, aber er _____ es nicht. (*want, can*)

d _____ du gut Skateboard fahren? – Nein, aber ich _____ es lernen. (*can, want*)

e Ich _____ Hausaufgaben machen, aber ich _____ sie nicht machen! (*should, want*)

f _____ du ins Kino gehen? – Nein, das _____ ich nicht. Ich _____ zu Hause bleiben. (*want, am allowed, must*)

kann	müssen
wollen	muss
will	kannst
darf	soll
willst	

The imperfect tense

The imperfect tense, for example *war* (was), *hatte* (had), is used for descriptions in the past.

sein: ich war, du warst, er/sie/es war, wir waren, ihr wart, sie/Sie waren

haben: ich hatte, du hattest, er/sie/es hatte, wir hatten, ihr hattet, sie/Sie hatten

2 **Change the present tense of *haben* or *sein* in these sentences into the imperfect. (The words you need are in the box below right.)**

a Ich habe einen Computer. __Ich hatte einen Computer.__

b Wir sind zu Hause. _____

c Hugo hat neue Schuhe. _____

d Sigrid ist nicht sehr gesund. _____

e Er hat einen Weihnachtskuchen. _____

f Wir haben viele Geschenke. _____

g Ich bin in der Schule. _____

h Bist du krank? _____

hatte
hatten
war
warst
waren

Grammar patterns

1 **This unit has practised some key grammar patterns.**

Pattern 1. Look at this sentence:

Ich finde Fasching cool, weil es Spaß macht.

What effect does the word *weil* have on the sentence?

_____

2 **Prove that you have understood by joining each pair of sentences with *weil*:**

a Ich mag Weihnachten. Man bekommt Geschenke.

_____

b Ich finde Ostern toll. Ich mag Schokolade.

_____

c Nina mag Partys nicht. Sie sind zu laut.

_____

3 **Pattern 2. Now look at this sentence:**

Ich muss eine neue Hose kaufen.

What effect does the verb *müssen* have on the sentence?

_____

Which four other modal verbs have you learnt, apart from *müssen*?

_____ _____ _____ _____

4 **Prove that you have understood by writing out each sentence as a longer sentence, using the modal verb supplied:**

a Ich backe Kuchen.

Ich kann ____Kuchen____ ____backen____ .

b Wir gehen zur Party.

Wir dürfen _____ _____ _____ .

c Ali macht Hausaufgaben.

Ali muss _____ _____ .

d Ich gehe ins Kino.

Ich will _____ _____ _____ .

e Du parkst hier nicht.

Du sollst _____ _____ .

1B Vokabular

Feiertage und Feste — *National holidays and festivals*

Fasching	*Carnival*
Heiligabend	*Christmas Eve*
Neujahr	*New Year*
Ostern	*Easter*
Rhein in Flammen	*Rhine in Flames*
Silvester	*New Year's Eve*
Tag der Deutschen Einheit	*Day of German Unity*
Weihnachten	*Christmas*
Wann feiert man …?	*When do you celebrate …?*
Man feiert am (+ *date*) …	*We celebrate … on the (+ date).*
Wie findest du …?	*What do you think of …?*
Ich finde … klasse.	*I think … is great.*
stark	*great, really cool, wicked*
supergut	*fantastic, excellent*

Party machen — *Organising a party*

Ich muss …	*I must …*
Einladungen schreiben.	*write invitations.*
Kuchen backen.	*bake cakes.*
Musik auswählen.	*choose some music.*
ein Outfit kaufen.	*buy an outfit.*
das Zimmer dekorieren.	*decorate the room.*
Essen kaufen.	*buy food.*
aufräumen.	*tidy up.*
Man kann … im Supermarkt kaufen.	*You can buy … in the supermarket.*
in der Bäckerei	*at the baker's*
im Modegeschäft/ Musikgeschäft	*at the clothes shop/ music shop*
Man kann …	*You can …*
Karaoke singen.	*sing karaoke.*
Spaß haben.	*have fun.*
mit Freunden reden.	*chat with friends.*
tanzen.	*dance.*
essen/trinken.	*eat/drink.*

Nichts als Ausreden — *Excuses, excuses …*

Ich mache eine Strandparty.	*I'm having a beach party.*
Kommst du?	*Will you come?*
Ja, gern. Vielen Dank für die Einladung.	*Yes, I'd love to. Thanks very much for the invitation.*
Nein, ich darf leider nicht kommen.	*No, unfortunately I'm not allowed to come.*
Ich soll …	*I'm supposed to …*
Hausaufgaben machen.	*do my homework.*
mein Zimmer aufräumen.	*tidy my room.*
zu Hause helfen.	*help at home.*
im Garten arbeiten.	*work in the garden.*
auf meine Geschwister aufpassen.	*look after my brothers and sisters.*

Die Party war spitze! — *The party was great!*

langweilig	*boring*
spitze/toll	*great*
der totale Hammer	*totally cool, awesome*
Ich hatte hundert Gäste.	*I had a hundred guests.*
Es gab …	*There was/were …*
eine Karaoke-Anlage.	*a karaoke machine.*
leckeres Essen.	*delicious food.*
nette Gäste.	*nice guests.*
tolle Musik.	*great music.*
Ich habe …	*I …*
Einladungen geschrieben.	*wrote invitations.*
Musik ausgewählt.	*chose some music.*
das Studio dekoriert.	*decorated the studio.*
Essen gekauft.	*bought food.*
gebacken.	*baked.*
Wir/Die Gäste haben …	*We/The guests …*
Musik gehört.	*listened to music.*
gesungen/getanzt.	*sang/danced.*
gefeiert/gegessen/ getrunken.	*celebrated/ate/drank …*

Checklist

How well do you think you can do the following? Write a sentence for each one if you can.			
	I can do this well	I can do this but not very well	I can't do this yet
1. talk about national holidays and festivals			
2. talk about organising a party and describe a party I've been to			
3. accept or decline an invitation, and give excuses			
4. use modal verbs			
5. use the imperfect tense and the perfect tense			
6. use different strategies to help with listening			

1 Work out what type of programme each one is and write it in.

TV Heute – Samstag, 25. Juni

15.00 Blitz-Info
Nachrichten

19.00 Meyerstraße
_____

22.00 Rocktastisch
_____

15.30 Fragen, Fragen
_____

19.30 Maxi Maus
_____

23.00 Handball
_____

16.30 Bist du ein Star?
_____

20.00 Infos um acht
_____

18.00 Tiger in Indien
_____

20.30 Kleine Schwester
_____

Realityshow
Musiksendung
Nachrichten
Quizsendung
Sportsendung
Seifenoper
Castingshow
Dokumentarserie
Zeichentrickserie

2 Work with a partner. Say what kind of TV show you want to watch.
Your partner should guide you to the appropriate show.

Example: **A** Ich will eine Seifenoper sehen.

B Es gibt „Meyerstraße" um 19 Uhr.

1 Unjumble these anagrams of technology-related words. When you have worked them out, write them in the grid. What's the missing word in the tinted box down?

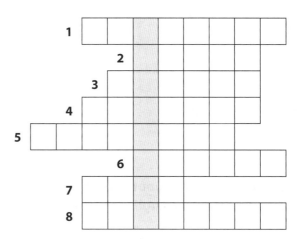

1 AKOECOFB   *Facebook* _____

2 NYAHD _____

3 ATPLPO _____

4 TDPOANE _____

5 ENNITRET _____

6 NENOLI _____

7 PIOD _____

8 MTPUEOCR _____

Missing word: _____

2 Look again at the words in the grid above and answer these questions.

a What do you notice about the words (in view of the fact that you are learning German)?

_____

b Which do you think is the odd one out, and why?

_____

c By contrast, what do you notice about these words relating to 'old media': *Fernsehen, Zeitung, Schreibmaschine, Brief*?

_____

d In what way is the word *Brief* a false friend?

_____

2A.3 Techno ist toll!

1 *Musikquiz.* **Find 12 music-related words in this wordsearch.**

Indie	Blues
Folk	Disco
Electronica	Funk
House	Rock
Dubstep	Pop
Techno	Reggae

D	U	B	S	T	E	P	Ä	Ü
I	Ä	L	Ä	Ü	L	O	Ü	Ä
S	Ö	U	Ö	Ä	E	P	Ä	K
C	Ä	E	Ü	Ö	C	Ä	C	Ü
O	Ö	S	Ä	Ö	T	O	Ä	Ö
Ä	Ü	Ä	Ö	Ü	R	Ä	Ü	Ä
F	O	L	K	H	O	U	S	E
U	T	E	C	H	N	O	Ö	Ä
N	Ü	I	N	D	I	E	Ü	Ö
K	Ä	Ü	Ä	Ö	C	Ö	Ä	Ü
Ä	R	E	G	G	A	E	Ü	Ö

2 **Read the article below about a footballer. Fill the gaps in this summary with suitable English words.**

Heiko is a ___footballer___ but he also likes _____ .

His favourite kind is _____ , but it's not good for his

_____ .

He can also _____ and play _____ . He doesn't

like _____ music because it's _____ and

_____ . He prefers music which is _____ and

_____ , just like _____ .

Heiko Heimlich spielt Fußball in der Bundesliga, aber er mag auch gern Musik.

– Heiko, welche Musik hörst du am liebsten?

– Also, ich höre besonders gern Techno. Hier in Berlin gibt es viele Techno-Clubs, wo man die ganze Nacht tanzen kann. Das ist natürlich nicht gut für mein Trainingsprogramm!

– Kannst du singen?

– Ja, ganz gut. Ich singe manchmal Karaoke. Ich kann auch Gitarre spielen, aber nicht sehr gut.

– Welche Musik gefällt dir nicht?

– Klassische Musik höre ich nicht gern, weil diese Musik zu langsam und zu leise ist. Techno und Metal finde ich besser, weil sie laut und schnell sind, wie Fußball!

2A.4 Wie war der Film?

1 🎧 **Listen to Anne and Leo discussing what film to see and fill in the grid. For each film, note the type of film, the country it comes from, the cinema showing it, and what they say about it.**

Film	Type	Country	Cinema	Described as
Der Blaue Planet				
Mein Schatz				
Lachen in Lyon				

2 **Imagine you have seen the three films mentioned in Activity 1. Write what you thought of each one. Use this pattern:**

1 Ich habe _____ (*film title*) gesehen. Das war ein(e)

_____ (*film type*). Der Film hat mir (nicht) gefallen, weil

er _____ (*description*) war.

2 _____

_____

_____

3 _____

_____

_____

1 **Look at these reading materials. How would you describe each one? Copy the correct words from the box on the right.**

Sachbuch

Mädchenzeitschrift

Liebesroman

Kinderbuch

Krimi

Sportmagazin

_____

_____

_____

_____

_____

_____

2 🎧 **Listen to the results of a radio survey about young people's reading habits. Note the results in the grid, in the order you hear them.**

Percentage %	Type of reading material (in English)
15	romantic novels

Possessive adjectives

	masculine	feminine	neuter	plural
my	mein	meine	mein	meine
your	dein	deine	dein	deine
his	sein	seine	sein	seine
her	ihr	ihre	ihr	ihre

1 **Circle the correct form of the possessive adjective in each sentence.**

a Sein / (Seine) Brille ist kaputt. (*fem.*)

b War deine / dein Essen okay? (*neuter*)

c Sein / Seine Lieblingssänger ist Bruno Mars. (*masc.*)

d Mein / Meine Lieblingssendung ist X Factor. (*fem.*)

e Ihr / Ihre Lieblingsfilm ist Toy Story. (*masc.*)

f Ist das deine / dein Handy? (*neuter*)

g Mein / Meine Freunde sind alle nett. (*plural*)

h Sie heißt Manja und das ist ihre / ihr Freundin. (*fem.*)

2 **Use *diese*, *dieses* or *diese* to complete these sentences.**

a _____Dieses_____ Eis schmeckt toll. (*neuter*)

b _____ Sänger kann nicht gut singen. (*masc.*)

c _____ Buch ist interessant. (*neuter*)

d _____ Laptops sind viel zu teuer. (*plural*)

e _____ Webseite ist neu. (*fem.*)

f _____ Musik ist sehr laut. (*fem.*)

g _____ Film ist altmodisch. (*masc.*)

h _____ Boygroups sind furchtbar. (*plural*)

Demonstrative adjectives

The words *dieser/diese/dieses/diese* can be used in place of *der/die/das/die* if you want to say 'this' or 'that', 'these' or 'those'.

masculine:	dieser
feminine:	diese
neuter:	dieses
plural:	diese

Die Sprache der Technologie

The language of technology is international. Because many of the products originated in America, English words are often used in other languages such as German. What often changes, however, is the pronunciation.

1 Say these words out loud in the way they would be pronounced by a German speaker.

🎧 Check by listening to the recording.

Webseite	Medien
Internet	Blog
Videoclip	Laptop
Facebook	chatten
MP3-Player	Kanal
Handy	

2 Copy the technology words in Activity 1 into the three categories in the table below.

Exactly the same as in English	Similar to English words	Completely different

3 Draw lines to join the opposites.

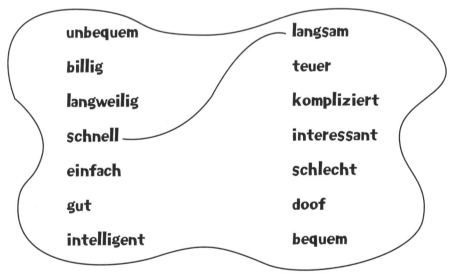

unbequem	langsam
billig	teuer
langweilig	kompliziert
schnell	interessant
einfach	schlecht
gut	doof
intelligent	bequem

Are any of the words new to you? Look for clues as to what they mean. If stumped, use a dictionary.

4 Which pair was simplest to guess, in your opinion?

2A Vokabular

Im Fernsehen	On TV
eine Castingshow	a talent show
eine Dokumentarserie	a documentary
eine Musiksendung	a music programme
die Nachrichten	the news
eine Quizsendung	a quiz show
eine Realityshow	a reality show
eine Seifenoper	a soap opera
eine Sportsendung	a sports programme
eine Zeichentrickserie	a cartoon
Ich sehe (nicht) gern …	I (don't) like watching …
Meine Lieblingssendung ist …	My favourite programme is …

Neue Medien, alte Medien	New media, old media
das Chatten auf Skype	chatting on Skype
der Fernseher	television set
das Handy, das Telefon	mobile phone, telephone
die Schreibmaschine	typewriter
die Tageszeitung	daily paper
Ich höre Radio auf meinem Player/iPod.	I listen to the radio on my MP3 player/iPod.
Ich sehe Filme auf meinem Computer.	I watch films on my computer.
Ich lese im Internet.	I read on the internet.
Ich lade Videoclips aus dem Internet herunter.	I download video clips from the internet.
Ich chatte mit Freunden im Internet.	I chat with friends on Facebook.
weil das schnell/langsam geht	because it's fast/slow
bequem	convenient
billig, teuer	cheap, expensive
einfach, kompliziert	easy, complicated
langweilig	boring
praktisch, unpraktisch	practical, impractical
Das kostet nichts/viel.	It costs nothing/a lot.

morgens, mittags	in the mornings, at midday
nachmittags, abends	in the afternoons/evenings
jeden Tag/Abend, jede Woche	every day/evening/week
oft, manchmal, selten, nie	often, sometimes, seldom, never

Techno ist toll!	Techno is great!
Welcher/Welche/Welches … gefällt dir (am besten)?	Which … do you like (best)?
… gefällt mir gut/gar nicht.	I like … /don't like … at all.
Ich höre am liebsten …	I prefer listening to …
die Band, die Gruppe	band, group
das Lied	song
der Sänger/die Sängerin	singer (male/female)
der Schlagzeuger	drummer

Wie war der Film?	What was the film like?
Welchen Film hast du gesehen?	What film have you seen?
Ich habe … gesehen.	I saw …
Was für ein Film ist/war das?	What kind of film is/was it?
ein Actionfilm	an action film
ein Dokumentarfilm	a documentary
ein Fantasyfilm	a fantasy film
eine Komödie	a comedy
ein Liebesfilm	a love story
ein Musical	a musical
ein Science-Fiction-Film	a science fiction film
ein Zeichentrickfilm	a cartoon
Dieser Film gefällt mir	I like this film, …
Dieser Film hat mir (nicht) gefallen, …	I liked/didn't like this film …
weil er lustig ist/war.	because it is/was funny.
weil die Spezialeffekte toll sind/waren.	because the special effects are/were great.
die Geschichte	story/plot
der Schauspieler/die Schauspielerin	actor/actress
romantisch	romantic
spannend	exciting
unterhaltsam	entertaining

Checklist

How well do you think you can do the following? Write a sentence for each one if you can.	I can do this well	I can do this but not very well	I can't do this yet
1. talk about TV programmes, films, music, singers and bands			
2. talk about old and new forms of media			
3. talk about my reading habits			
4. use the perfect tense and the imperfect			
5. use strategies to help me understand longer texts			
6. pronounce the *ei* and *ie* sounds			

2B.1 Mein Lieblingshobby

1 **Write in the correct present tense form of *spielen* or *fahren*.**

fährt	fahre
spielt	spiele
spielen	spielst

a Ich _____spiele_____ oft Fußball.

b Mein Freund _____ Schlagzeug.

c _____ du Gitarre?

d Ich _____ gern Ski.

e Ich _____ auch gern Rad.

f Wir _____ im Sommer Tennis.

g Olaf _____ oft Skateboard.

h Er _____ auch Computerspiele.

2 **Identify the German leisure activity words from the English clues.**

a Skiing on water _____

b Rolling on shoes _____

c A kind of VW _____

d Bike for racing _____

e Tennis on a table _____

f A jazz instrument _____

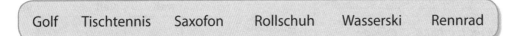

| Golf | Tischtennis | Saxofon | Rollschuh | Wasserski | Rennrad |

3 🎧 **Listen to Ben and Simone talking about their hobbies. Note the details in the grid, in English.**

	Ben	Simone
likes	Ice-skating	
reason		
doesn't like		
reason		

Christian: Mein Lieblingshobby ist Sport. Am Wochenende habe ich Tischtennis gespielt, aber ich habe nicht gewonnen. Wenn ich Zeit habe, spiele ich Golf mit meinem Vater oder ich gehe schwimmen, denn das Schwimmbad ist nicht weit von meinem Haus. Ich mag Tennis und ich fahre auch gern Rollschuh, weil das Spaß macht.

1   Read about Christian's hobbies. Underline all the connectives in the text.

2   Now write the German connectives next to their English meanings.

    a   whenever / if _____

    b   because (2 words) _____ _____

    c   but _____

    d   and _____

    e   or _____

3   Answer these questions about the text above.

    a   What did Christian do at the weekend?

    _____

    b   What was the result?

    _____

    c   Under what conditions does he play golf?

    _____

    d   Why is it easy for him to go swimming?

    _____

    e   Why does he like roller skating?

    _____

1 *Wetterquiz.* **Find these ten weather words in the grid.**

Gewitter	Schnee	Regen	Nebel	Wind
Sommer	heiß	warm	sonnig	kalt

A	K	O	N	N	M	G	H
T	S	S	C	H	N	E	E
H	S	O	M	M	E	W	I
Z	Ü	N	D	R	B	I	ß
W	I	N	D	J	E	T	S
A	L	I	K	A	L	T	C
R	E	G	E	N	Ü	E	H
M	S	O	M	M	E	R	B

2 **Fill the gaps in these sentences.**

a Wenn es _____kalt_____ 🌧️ ist, _____ ich Schlittschuh.

b Wenn es _____ ☀️ ist, _____ ich in den Park.

c Wenn es _____ 🌧️ , _____ ich zu Hause.

d Wenn es _____ 🌬️ ist, _____ ich mit dem Bus,
nicht mit dem Auto.

gehe
bleibe
fahre
fahre
regnet
neblig
kalt
warm

3 🎧 **Listen and fill in the grid in English with details about a family's activities in different seasons.**

Season	Weather	Destination	Activity
winter			

2B.4 Nächstes Wochenende

1 🎧 **Listen to three people who mention activities in the present, past and future. Fill in the grid in English.**

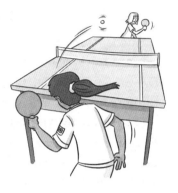

	Present	Past	Future
1	football		
2			
3			

2 **Unjumble these future tense sentences.**

a wird mit Leo fahren Bus dem

      Leo wird mit dem Bus fahren.

b gehen Sira Kino ins wird

_____

c werde Ich spielen Federball

_____

d Spaghetti werde kochen Ich

_____

e werden hören Rockmusik Wir

_____

f Skateboard morgen fahren werden Wir

_____

3 **Put these sentences into the future tense. Begin each one with *ich werde*.**

a Ich spiele Schlagzeug.

_____

b Ich spiele Basketball.

_____

c Ich lese eine Musikzeitschrift.

_____

2B.5 Ungewöhnliche Hobbys!

„ISCHA FREIMAAK!"

In Süddeutschland gibt es Karneval, aber in der norddeutschen Hafenstadt Bremen feiert man immer im Oktober Freimarkt.

Der große Rummelplatz ist hinter der Stadthalle und nicht weit vom Bürgerpark. Tausende von Menschen besuchen den Freimarkt. Es gibt Riesenkarussells und eine große Achterbahn.

Es gibt viel zu essen und zu trinken. Für die Kinder gibt es Pferdewürste, Zuckerwatte, Sahneeis, Pommes mit Mayo, Kartoffelpuffer mit Apfelmus, und für die Eltern gibt es Glühwein und viel Bier im Bayernzelt.

Wie beim Fasching gibt es einen großen Umzug durch die Innenstadt. Die Leute werfen Bonbons auf die Straße und die Kinder sind sehr glücklich!

1 **Read through the text above. It may seem a bit hard, but it's fun to work out meanings and it's easier than it seems, especially as the German language tends to put words together to make new ones. Try these activities to help you work out the unfamiliar words.**

a Bremen is quite near the sea. What do you think a *Hafenstadt* is?

_____

b We're talking about a festival, like *Karneval*. What could a *Rummelplatz* be?

_____

c Is the *Bürgerpark* somewhere to eat fast food? Look up *Bürger* in the

dictionary and work it out. _____

d What's a *Karussell*? It's like an English word. _____

e Guess what *Achterbahn* could mean. Remember *Bahn* means railway.

_____

f What's a *Pferdewurst*? _____

g If *Zucker* means 'sugar' and *Watte* means 'cotton wool', what is *Zuckerwatte*?

_____

h What is *Mayo* short for? _____

i What are *Kartoffelpuffer* made from and what do you eat with them?

_____

j What's special about *Glühwein*? _____

k Where in town is the *Innenstadt*? _____

l What makes the kids happy? _____

Adjective endings

When an adjective comes in front of a noun, it needs an extra ending:
-er, -e or -es.

Das ist/sind …

masculine ein toll**er** Fußball.

neuter ein toll**es** Buch.

feminine eine toll**e** CD.

plural neu**e** Schuhe.

---

1 **Circle the correct adjective in each sentence.**

a Ein neue / (neuer) Computer kostet viel Geld.

b Das ist mein neue / neues Auto.

c Das ist ein interessante / interessanter Film.

d Nena ist eine deutsches / deutsche Sängerin.

e Frankfurt ist eine große / großes Stadt.

f Das ist mein alter / altes Rad.

g Ein moderne / moderner MP3-Player ist nicht billig.

h Das war ein gutes / gute Spiel.

masculine	feminine	neuter
Film	Sängerin	Spiel
Player	Stadt	Auto
Computer		Rad

The future

To talk about the future, you can use the present tense of *werden* plus the main verb (in the infinitive) at the end of the sentence.

Ich spiele Tennis. (*I play tennis.*) ⟶ Ich **werde** Tennis spielen. (*I will play tennis.*)

---

2 **Circle the correct form of *werden* in these future tense sentences.**

a Wir wird / werden im Winter Ski fahren.

b Meine Mutter wird / wirst um 10 Uhr nach Hause kommen.

c Ich werden / werde eine Bratwurst kaufen.

d Was wirst / wird du heute Abend machen?

e Leo und Anna werde / werden Tennis spielen.

f Eine Indie-Band wirst / wird in der Stadthalle spielen.

g Ich wird / werde eine E-Mail schreiben.

ich werde
du wirst
er/sie/es wird
wir werden
ihr werdet
sie/Sie werden

Pronunciation

1 Try saying these words out loud. Some of them you haven't seen before but you can still pronounce them.

🎧 Listen to the recording to check and repeat.

a Wasser	**i** Verein	**q** Volker (*a man's name*)
b Wetter	**j** von	**r** Wiebke (*a girl's name*)
c Winter	**k** Wagen	**s** Wannsee (*a lake in Berlin*)
d vier	**l** Ingwer (*ginger*)	**t** Vogel (*bird*)
e Viertel	**m** Verden (*a town in north Germany*)	
f Vati	**n** Wolle (*wool*)	
g warm	**o** Möwe (*seagull*)	
h Gewitter	**p** vielleicht (*perhaps*)	

> **Remember ...**
> - a German **W** sounds like an English **V**
> - a German **V** sounds like an English **F**

Connectives

2 Fill in this grid to make a summary of the connectives you have learnt.

Word	Meaning	Sends verb to end? YES / NO
weil	because	yes
aber		
oder		
denn		
wenn		
und		

3 Make a ridiculously long sentence by adding connectives into all the gaps. It needs to make sense. Read it out, if you have enough breath!

> Gestern bin ich in den Supermarkt gegangen, ____weil____ ich Brot
>
> kaufen wollte, _____ es gab kein Brot, _____ der Ofen war
>
> kaputt _____ der Bäcker war krank, _____ vielleicht war
>
> er nicht krank _____ er war nicht da, _____ er faul war,
>
> _____ das war ein Problem, _____ ich Hunger hatte und
>
> _____ ich Hunger habe, bin ich böse!*

*böse – angry

2B Vokabular

Mein Lieblingshobby / **My favourite hobby**

Was machst du gern/nicht gern?	What do/don't you like doing?
Ich besuche Freunde.	I visit friends.
Ich fotografiere.	I do photography.
Ich höre Musik.	I listen to music.
Ich lese Bücher.	I read books.
Ich mache Leichtathletik/Sport.	I do athletics/sport.
Ich sammle Karten.	I collect cards.
Ich sehe fern.	I watch TV.
Ich singe in einem Chor.	I sing in a choir.
Ich spiele Theater.	I'm in a drama group.
Ich surfe im Internet.	I surf the internet.
Ich tanze.	I go dancing.

Ich spiele …	I play …
Computerspiele.	computer games.
Fußball.	football.
Gitarre.	guitar.
Golf.	golf.
Saxofon.	saxophone.
Schach.	chess.
Schlagzeug.	drums.
Tennis.	tennis.
Tischtennis.	table tennis.

Ich fahre …	I go …
Rad.	cycling.
Rennrad.	cycle racing.
Rollschuh.	roller-skating.
Schlittschuh.	ice-skating.
Skateboard.	skateboarding.
Ski.	skiing.
Wasserski.	waterskiing.

Das ist ein tolles Hobby! / **That's a great hobby!**

Mein Hobby ist/sind …	My hobby is …
Das ist ein tolles Hobby, …	It's a great hobby, …
Das Hobby macht Spaß, …	It's a fun hobby, …
weil es billig ist.	because it's cheap.
weil ich musikalisch/sportlich bin.	because I'm musical/sporty.
denn es ist interessant.	because it's interesting.
denn es ist ungewöhnlich.	because it's unusual.
aber es ist teuer.	but it's expensive.
aber ich habe keine Zeit für andere Hobbys.	but I have no time for other hobbies.

Wenn es heiß ist, … / **When the weather's hot, …**

Es ist heiß/kalt/sonnig/warm/windig	It's hot/cold/sunny/warm/windy
Es friert.	It's freezing.
Es gewittert.	It's stormy/There's thunder and lightning.
Es ist neblig.	It's foggy.
Es regnet.	It's raining.
Es schneit.	It's snowing.
im Frühling	in spring
im Sommer	in summer
im Herbst	in autumn
im Winter	in winter

Wenn es windig ist, gehe ich Windsurfen.	When it's windy, I go windsurfing.
Ich fahre Inliner, wenn es warm ist.	I go rollerblading when it's warm.

Nächstes Wochenende / **Next weekend**

Ich werde …	I will …
spät aufstehen.	get up late.
Musik hören.	listen to music.
Fußball spielen.	play football.
ein Musical singen.	sing in a musical.
ein Buch lesen.	read a book.
Inliner fahren.	go rollerblading.
fernsehen.	watch TV.
Gitarre spielen.	play guitar.
schwimmen.	go swimming.

Checklist

How well do you think you can do the following?

Write a sentence for each one if you can.

	I can do this well	I can do this but not very well	I can't do this yet
1. talk about my favourite hobby			
2. talk about what hobbies I do in different kinds of weather			
3. talk about what I will do next weekend			
4. use regular and irregular verbs in the present tense			
5. use the future tense			
6. use correct word order with linking words			

1 *Körperquiz.* **Use the picture clues to complete the crossword.**

Waagerecht (across)

1   2

4   5

6

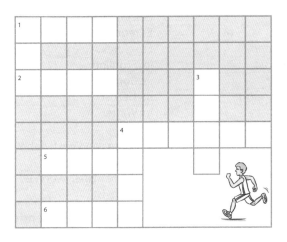

Senkrecht (down)

1   3

4

• Which of the answers is the odd one out, and why?

_____

2 **Which of these nouns are singular and which are plural? Write S or P next to each. (Watch out! One of the nouns is both S and P.)**

a Augen _____   e Ohr _____   i Zahn _____

b Nase _____   f Bein _____   j Fuß _____

c Beine _____   g Körper _____

d Köpfe _____   h Arme _____

3 **Possessive adjectives: circle the correct option in each sentence.**

a <u>Mein</u> / <u>Meine</u> Augen sind blau.

b Anja hat <u>sein</u> / <u>ihr</u> Bein gebrochen.

c <u>Dein</u> / <u>Deine</u> Füße sind sehr groß.

d Pinocchio ist aus Holz. Seine/Sein Nase ist lang.

e Martin ist sportlich. <u>Ihr</u> / <u>Sein</u> Körper ist muskulös.

f Gib mir <u>dein</u> / <u>deine</u> Hand.

1   Complete these sentences about ailments, using words from the box.

Zahnschmerzen
tut mir weh
Kopfschmerzen
Fieber
tut mir weh
Rückenschmerzen
Bauchschmerzen
Ohrenschmerzen

a   Ich habe _____ .

b   Ich habe _____ .

c   Mein Bein _____ .

d   Ich habe _____ .

e   Mein Arm _____ .

f   Ich habe _____ .

g   Ich habe _____ .

h   Ich habe _____ .

2   *Beim Arzt.* **Listen and work out what's wrong with the patient. Write YES or NO for each problem**

bad leg _____   headache _____   backache _____   bad arm _____

sore eyes _____   earache _____   sore feet _____   temperature _____

What's actually wrong with her? _____

3   *seit* = **since / for**
Decide whether seit means 'since' or 'for' in these sentences.

a   Ich bin seit Mittwoch in Hannover.   _____

b   Wir sind seit drei Wochen zu Hause.   _____

c   Udo spielt seit drei Jahren Fußball.   _____

d   Marina ist seit Montag krank.   _____

e   Ich warte hier seit neun Uhr.   _____

3A.3 Topfit!

1 **Draw lines to link up the sentence halves.**

a Leo geht zum Bäcker,   um zu essen.

b Boris geht ins Restaurant,   um ein Auto zu kaufen.

c Wir gehen zur Schule,   um im Internet zu surfen.

d Wir spielen Basketball,   um Brot zu kaufen.

e Ich kaufe einen Computer,   um zu lernen.

f Onkel Jochen spart Geld,   um fit zu bleiben.

2 🎧 **Listen and take notes in English: what does the speaker do, when and what for?**

	Activity	When?	What for?
1	walks the dog		
2			
3			
4			
5			

3 **Translate these expressions of frequency into English.**

a zweimal pro Woche _____

b nie _____

c oft _____

d manchmal _____

e selten _____

f einmal pro Monat _____

g sechsmal pro Jahr _____

h dreimal pro Tag _____

3A.4 Du bist, was du isst!

1 Complete the table: translate the foods into English and write *JA* if they are healthy and *NEIN* if not.

Deutsch	Englisch	gesund? JA / NEIN
Schwarzbrot	rye bread	
Pommes		
Milch		
Gemüse		
Wurst		
Chips		
Süßigkeiten		
Obst		
Mineralwasser		
Kekse		

2 🎧 Listen to six radio adverts and health tips. Answer the questions in English.

1a What is it encouraging you to drink? _____

1b Why? _____

2a Who is speaking? _____

2b What is the advice? _____

2c Why? _____

3a What should you do? _____

3b Why? _____

4a What is it encouraging you to do? _____

4b Why? _____

5a Who is giving advice? _____

5b What is the advice? _____

5c Why? _____

6a What is the advice? _____

6b Why? _____

• Which adverts offer <u>healthy</u> advice? Write the numbers. _____

1 Sort out the food words on the right into the correct grid columns.

Gemüse	Obst	Milchprodukte	Fisch	Fleisch
Brokkoli				

Kartoffeln   Butter
Lamm   Wurst
Sardellen   Brokkoli
Käse   Makrele
Schinken   Joghurt
Aprikosen   Rotkohl
Krabben   Äpfel
Erdbeeren

2 Read the problem page letter and answer. Are the sentences below true (T), false (F) or not mentioned (NM)?

a Maria would like to go dancing.   **T**

b Karin used to be overweight.   _____

c Karin drinks lemonade.   _____

d It's OK to drink cola.   _____

e Chips are bad for you.   _____

f You can eat bread and butter.   _____

g Three portions of fruit and vegetables a day are recommended.   _____

h Playing football would help.   _____

i Walking would help.   _____

j Soon Maria's friends will be laughing at her.   _____

Liebe Karin,

ich habe ein Problem. Ich bin sechzehn und ich bin übergewichtig*. Ich kann nicht schnell laufen oder tanzen und meine Freundinnen lachen über mich. Was soll ich tun? Maria

Liebe Maria,

ich verstehe dein Problem. Ich war früher auch übergewichtig aber jetzt bin ich schlank und gesund. Es ist wichtig, viel Wasser zu trinken. Vergiss Limonade und Cola, diese Getränke sind viel zu süß. Bonbons, Chips und Hamburger sind natürlich auch „out". Alles, was viel Fett und Zucker hat, ist schlecht für deinen Körper.

Es ist wichtig, täglich Schwarzbrot (ohne Butter) zu essen, und auch viel Obst und Gemüse (mindestens drei Portionen pro Tag).

Aber Essen ist nicht dein einziges Problem. Du sollst auch mehr Sport machen. Joggen, Tischtennis, sogar spazieren gehen: alles ist gut für die Gesundheit (mindestens 20 Minuten pro Tag).

Bald wirst du mit deinen Freundinnen wieder tanzen gehen, und sie werden nicht mehr über dich lachen!

Karin

*übergewichtig *overweight*

1 **Translate these sentences into English.**

a Ich bin seit Montag krank.

I've been ill since Monday.

b Wir wohnen seit sechs Jahren in diesem Haus.

_____

c Leo arbeitet seit drei Monaten bei Radio Zoom.

_____

d Wir sind seit einer Woche auf einem Campingplatz in Irland.

_____

e Ich habe seit vier Tagen Grippe.

_____

> **seit**
> The word *seit* means either 'since' or 'for'. It means 'since' a specific time or 'for' a period of time. In English, complicated tenses are used ('I have been living here for …'). In German, it's much simpler – just use the present tense.

> **The imperative**
> If you want to tell someone what to do or give a command in German, you use the imperative form:
> (*du*)　　　**Trink** mehr Wasser. _Drink more water._
> (*Sie*)　　　**Trinken Sie** mehr Wasser. _Drink more water._

2 **Which of these orders are being given to a friend (F) and which to a stranger (S)?**

a Steh auf! 　　 F

b Kommen Sie mit! _____

c Sprich Deutsch! _____

d Sag, was du willst! _____

e Bleiben Sie hier! _____

f Kaufen Sie Hammis Hamburger! _____

3 **Find the correct ending to each sentence and copy it in.**

a Wir gehen ins Kino, _____ .

b Anne nimmt den Bus, _____ .

c Oma geht zur Post, _____ .

d Wir gehen ins Konzert, _____ .

e Ich gehe jetzt ins Bett, _____ .

f Ich jogge, _____ .

> **um … zu …**
> Use *um … zu …* to say why you do something. It means 'in order to …'
> Put *um* at the beginning of the second clause (after the comma), and put *zu* at the end followed by an infinitive:
> Wir machen oft Sport, **um** fit **zu bleiben**. *We often do sport, (in order) to stay fit.*

> um zu schlafen　　　　um fit zu bleiben
> um einen Film zu sehen　　um Musik zu hören
> um nach Hause zu kommen　um ein Paket zu schicken

Adapting language

1 **Use patterns learnt in this unit to make new sentences.**

Pattern 1: Ich habe Bauchschmerzen.
Write three more sentences about aches and pains.

_____

_____

_____

Pattern 2: Mein Bein tut weh.
Write three more sentences about things that hurt.

_____

_____

_____

Pattern 3: Ich bin seit einer Stunde hier.
Write three more sentences about how long you have been somewhere.

_____

_____

_____

Pattern 4: Ich spiele Golf, um fit zu bleiben.
Write three sentences about things you do to stay healthy or slim.

_____

_____

_____

Pattern 5: Trink Limonade!
Write three more slogans for unhealthy food or drink.

_____

_____

_____

Pattern 6: Trinken Sie Limonade!
Now do it again, using the polite form.

_____

_____

_____

Pattern 7: Ich esse dreimal pro Tag Gemüse.
Write three more sentences about how often you do things.

_____

_____

> Here are some expressions to help you, but feel free to choose your own.
>
> Bauch
> Bein
> Fuß
> Kopf
> Hals
> Rücken
> Arm
> Hand
> seit einer Stunde
> seit einer Woche
> seit drei Tagen
> ich spiele ...
> ich esse ...
> ich mache ...
> Cola
> Pommes
> Chips
> Bonbons
> Hamburger
> oft
> immer
> nie
> manchmal
> einmal/zweimal/dreimal
> pro Stunde/Tag/Monat

Der Körper	The body
der Arm (-e)	arm
das Auge (-n)	eye
das Bein (-e)	leg
der Finger (-)	finger
der Fuß (Füße)	foot
die Hand (Hände)	hand
das Knie (-)	knee
der Kopf (Köpfe)	head
der Körper (-)	body
der Mund (Münder)	mouth
die Nase (-n)	nose
das Ohr (-en)	ear
der Zahn (Zähne)	tooth

Was fehlt dir?	What's wrong?
Ich habe ...	I have ...
Bauchschmerzen	stomach ache
Halsschmerzen	a sore throat
Knieschmerzen	a sore knee
Kopfschmerzen	a headache
Ohrenschmerzen	earache
Rückenschmerzen	backache
Zahnschmerzen	toothache
Fieber	a fever, a high temperature
eine Grippe	flu
Wie geht es dir?	How are you?
Es geht mir (nicht) gut.	I'm (not) well.
Ich bin krank.	I'm ill.
Mein Bein tut weh.	My leg hurts.
Ich habe mir die Nase gebrochen.	I've broken my nose.
Ich habe eine Allergie gegen Katzen.	I'm allergic to cats.
Ich habe Migräne.	I've got a migraine.
seit einer Woche/vier Tagen	for a week/four days
Es tut mir leid.	I'm sorry.

Topfit!	Superfit!
Ich mache ...	I do ...
Karate/Pilates.	karate/Pilates.
Sport/Yoga.	sport/yoga.
Ich spiele ...	I play ...
Basketball.	basketball.
Tischtennis.	table tennis.
Volleyball.	volleyball.
Ich jogge.	I go jogging.
Ich gehe (mit dem Hund) spazieren.	I go walking (with the dog).
Ich gehe zu Fuß in die Schule.	I walk to school.
Ich mache Sport, um fit zu bleiben.	I do sport in order to keep fit.
hin und wieder	now and then

manchmal	sometimes
nie	never
oft	often
selten	seldom
einmal/zweimal pro Woche	once/twice a week
dreimal pro Monat	three times a month

Du bist, was du isst!	You are what you eat!
die Chips	crisps
die Cola	cola
das Eis	ice cream
das Fastfood	fast food
das Gemüse	vegetables
der Käse	cheese
die Kekse	biscuits, cookies
die Milch	milk
das Obst	fruit
die Pommes	chips
die Süßigkeiten	sweets
das Mineralwasser	mineral water
das Schwarzbrot	rye bread
das Weißbrot	white bread
die Wurst	sausage

Ich esse normalerweise/ oft/selten/nie ...	I usually/often/rarely/never eat ...
Iss kein Fastfood!	Don't eat fast food!
Trinken Sie viel Wasser!	Drink lots of water!

Checklist

How well do you think you can do the following?			
Write a sentence for each one if you can.			
	I can do this well	I can do this but not very well	I can't do this yet
1. name parts of the body			
2. talk about illness and injuries			
3. talk about what sports I do to keep fit			
4. talk about healthy eating			
5. use possessive adjectives			
6. use seit			

1 **Complete the sentences with phrases from the box. Use your powers of logic!**

a Wir haben Hunger. Wir brauchen ___eine Liste von Restaurants.___

b Wir wollen schlafen. Wir brauchen _____

c Hotels sind zu teuer. Wir brauchen _____

d Campingplätze sind zu kalt. Wir brauchen _____

e Aber wo ist die Jugendherberge? Wir brauchen _____

f Wir müssen mit dem Bus fahren. Wir brauchen _____

g Wir wissen nichts über Düsseldorf. Wir brauchen _____

> eine Broschüre über die Stadt
> eine Liste von Hotels
> eine Liste von Jugendherbergen
> einen Stadtplan
> einen Fahrplan
> eine Liste von Campingplätzen
> eine Liste von Restaurants

2 **Read this letter to a tourist information office. Find the German equivalent for phrases a–i. Some may be new to you but they are easy to guess.**

> Sehr geehrte Damen und Herren,
>
> wir werden im Oktober nach Münster fahren, denn wir haben gehört, dass die Stadt besonders schön ist. Können Sie bitte ein paar Fragen beantworten?
>
> Wir sind vier Personen, ich, meine Frau und unsere zwei Kinder (8 und 6 Jahre). Hotels sind leider zu teuer für uns. Gibt es vielleicht eine Jugendherberge in der Stadt?
>
> Was gibt es in Münster zu sehen und zu tun? Vergessen Sie bitte nicht, dass die Kinder noch klein sind und sich nicht für Museen und Kunstgalerien interessieren. Gibt es einen Park und vielleicht einen Zoo?
>
> Wir möchten gern eine Broschüre über die Sehenswürdigkeiten und auch, wenn möglich, eine Liste von Restaurants. Natürlich brauchen wir auch einen Stadtplan.
>
> Vielen Dank im Voraus.
>
> Mit freundlichen Grüßen,
>
> Axel Müller

a we have heard: _wir haben gehört_

b particularly nice: _____

c a few: _____

d unfortunately: _____

e perhaps: _____

f art gallery: _____

g if possible: _____

h of course: _____

i in advance: _____

● Explain why *ein paar* is a false friend. _____

3 **On separate paper, write a similar letter to a tourist office in a different town. Change the enquiries if you like. Use some of the phrases from Activity 2 to make your letter sound as natural as possible.**

3B.2 Was kann man machen?

1 🎧 **Listen and answer the questions with YES or NO.**

a Is Zürich in Germany?   _No_

b Is it a good place to go shopping?   _____

c Are the hotels cheap?   _____

d Is the best youth hostel in the town centre? _____

e Is there plenty of entertainment?   _____

f Did Carsten go and see a live band?   _____

2 **Look at these phrases. Do they mean *in* or *into* the place mentioned?**

a im Park   _in_

b ins Kino   _____

c ins Museum   _____

d im Fernsehturm   _____

e in der Bahnhofstraße   _____

f in den Zoo   _____

g in die Stadt   _____

h in der Bäckerei   _____

> in = *im / in der*
> into = *in den / in die / ins*

3 **Make a list of things people can do in your town. Use vocabulary you know from this module and look up any extra words you need. Mention at least five things.**

Man kann _____

Man kann _____

Man _____

_____

_____

1 🎧 **Listen to identify the places on the town plan and write them in.**

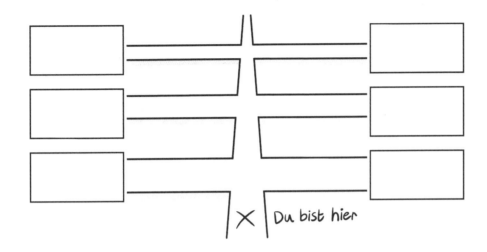

Stadtpark
Stadion
Post
Bahnhof
Jugendzentrum
U-Bahn-Station

X | Du bist hier

2 **Study the train journey information and (right) answer the questions.**

a Is this a single or return ticket?

Journey 1: _____ Journey 2: _____

b What class is it in?

Journey 1: _____ Journey 2: _____

c Does the passenger have to change?

Journey 1: _____ Journey 2: _____

3 **Make up dialogues with a partner.**

a Make a street map like the one in Activity 1. Direct your partner to places of your choice. Check that he/she has got them right.

Example: **A** *Geh geradeaus und nimm die erste Straße rechts.*
B *Ist das der Bahnhof?*
A *Ja, richtig!*

b Make up two dialogues at the station ticket counter, where the traveller buys a ticket for each journey in Activity 2.

Example: **A** *Wann fährt der Zug nach Oldenburg, bitte?*
B *Um neun Uhr dreißig.*
A *Eine Fahrkarte bitte, hin und zurück, erste Klasse.*
B *Ja, das kostet 27 Euro 50.*
A *Wo fährt der Zug ab?*
B *Von Gleis 4.*

1

Hamburg–Oldenburg
(hin und zurück)

Direkt	Hin:
	Zurück:	Gleis 4, 9:30 Uhr
1. Kl.		Gleis 12, 14:22 Uhr

€ Preis: €27,50

2

Frankfurt–Stuttgart
(über Mannheim, einfache Fahrt)

2. Kl. | Gleis 3, 16:46 Uhr

€ Preis: €33,30

3B.4   Wieder zu Hause!

1   **Describe the room: complete each sentence with three words from the box.**

a   Der Computer ist ___auf___ ___dem___ ___Tisch___ .

b   Die Katze ist _____ _____ _____ .

c   Das Buch ist _____ _____ _____ .

d   Die Schuhe sind _____ _____ .

e   Die Pflanze ist _____ _____ _____ .

f   Der Rucksack ist _____ _____ _____ .

auf	dem	Stuhl / Tisch
unter	der	Pflanze / Tür
hinter		
neben		

2   **Fill in the appropriate past participles.**

a   Wir haben einen neuen Computer ____gekauft____ .

b   Hast du den Film _____ ?

c   Emma hat im Meer _____ .

d   Ich habe bis drei Uhr morgens _____ .

e   Oma und Opa haben das Schloss _____ .

f   Wir haben in einem griechischen Restaurant _____ .

g   Ali ist mit dem Rad _____ .

h   Er ist um acht Uhr _____ .

i   Ich habe noch nie Cola _____ .

j   Na, was hast du _____ ?

gesehen
gekauft
besichtigt
getanzt
gefahren
angekommen
getrunken
gemacht
gegessen
geschwommen

3   **Look around you. Describe where some things are in your room or classroom. Use *auf, in, unter, neben, vor, hinter* or *zwischen*. For 'the', use *dem* with masculine and neuter nouns, *der* with feminine ones.**

_____

_____

_____

_____

Kronberg

Kronberg im Taunus grüßt Sie!

Attraktionen: Das Schloss ist morgens und nachmittags für Besucher geöffnet, von 9 Uhr bis 12 Uhr 30 und von 14 Uhr 30 bis 18 Uhr. Eintritt: Erwachsene €3, Kinder €1. Das Schloss-Restaurant ist momentan wegen Renovierungsarbeiten* geschlossen.

Der Golfplatz ist täglich von 7 Uhr bis 20 Uhr geöffnet. Besucher sind willkommen (nur Erwachsene).

Das öffentliche Freibad ist von Mai bis Oktober geöffnet. Eintritt: Erwachsene €5, Kinder €2. Der Freibad-Imbiss bietet Bockwurst mit Kartoffelsalat.

In der Stadtmitte befinden sich mehrere Einkaufsstraßen. Hier findet man schicke Boutiquen, nette Restaurants und Lokale, Supermärkte und Souvenirläden. In der Regel sind alle Geschäfte mittags geschlossen.

Kronberg ist von einem herrlichen Wald umgeben. Hier kann man wandern oder Mountainbike fahren.

Weitere Informationen erhalten Sie im Informationsbüro, Katharinenstraße 7.

*Renovierungsarbeiten – *renovation work*

1 **Read the web page about Kronberg and answer these true or false questions (T or F).**

a You can go to the castle at lunchtime.   `F`

b You can have afternoon tea at the castle.   ☐

c You can play golf with your children.   ☐

d You can go swimming in May.   ☐

e There's a wide range of food at the swimming pool snack bar.   ☐

f Kronberg is great for shopping.   ☐

g You can buy souvenirs at 3 pm.   ☐

h It's a great area for hiking.   ☐

i Mountain biking isn't allowed.   ☐

j You can get more information online.   ☐

2 **For any sentences you identified as false, add notes to explain why.**

These prepositions are always followed by the **dative** (m. *dem*, f. *der*, n. *dem*):

seit zu nach von mit aus

Remember that *zu dem* is shortened to *zum*.

These prepositions are followed by the **dative** (m. *dem*, f. *der*, n. *dem*) if there is <u>no</u> movement and the accusative (m. *den*, f. *die*, n. *das*) if there <u>is</u> movement:

in auf hinter neben vor unter zwischen

Remember that *in dem* is shortened to *im* and *in das* is shortened to *ins*.

1 🎧 **Listen carefully to these people. Are they talking about where they <u>are</u> or where they <u>are going</u>?**

1 (are)/ are going

2 are / are going

3 are / are going

4 are / are going

5 are / are going

6 are / are going

2 **Fill in the gaps with *den, die, das, der* or *dem*.**

a Wir fahren mit _____*dem*_____ Bus.

b Wir sind seit _____ Sommer hier.

c Gehst du in _____ Schule?

d Sira kocht in _____ Küche einen Kaffee.

e Jens kommt morgen aus _____ Krankenhaus?

f Leg das Buch auf _____ Tisch.

g Das Restaurant ist neben _____ Bäckerei.

h Was machst du nach _____ Schule?

i Wir kommen aus _____ Schweiz.

j Leo legt das Buch auf _____ Regal.

masculine	feminine	neuter
Bus	Schule	Krankenhaus
Sommer	Bäckerei	Sportzentrum
Tisch	Schweiz	Regal
	Küche	

Reading different text styles

1 Read the text extracts, decide which category they belong to, and write the letter of each extract in the right places.

Instructions: _____

Formal letter: _____

Informal letter: _____

Book/Literary text: _____

Newspaper article: _____

Magazine article: _____

(a)
Hallo Ahmed!

Hast du Lust, am Wochenende
ins Hallenbad zu gehen?

Pinar

(b) Können Sie uns bitte eine Broschüre schicken?

(c) **Bitte den Rasen nicht betreten!**

(d) Rotkäppchen hat den Wolf gesehen und hatte Angst.

(e) Nächste Woche in Top-Teen:
Ein tolles INTERVIEW mit Sebastian Vettel

(f) In der Innenstadt hat man am Freitag in ein Juweliergeschäft eingebrochen.

Working out missing words

2 Use your powers of logic to fill the gaps. Only one word suits each gap.

Sira und ich sind am letzten _Samstag_ mit _____

Bus nach Kronberg _____. Zuerst sind wir

_____ Schloss gegangen. Es war_____ schön,

aber ein bisschen _____. Wir hatten _____,

aber das Restaurant war _____. Am _____

sind wir einkaufen _____. Die Geschäfte

_____ langweilig, absolut nichts für _____

Leute. Also sind wir in den _____ gegangen. Das

Wandern hat _____ gemacht, aber am Abend waren wir

_____ müde.

Spaß
gefahren
Hunger
Samstag
dem
Wald
zum
waren
ziemlich
geschlossen
altmodisch
junge
gegangen
Nachmittag
sehr

Wir brauchen Infos! / *We need info!*

Wir brauchen …	*We need …*
eine Broschüre über die Stadt.	*a brochure about the town.*
einen Fahrplan.	*a timetable.*
eine Liste von billigen Hotels/Restaurants.	*a list of cheap hotels/ restaurants.*
eine Liste von Campingplätzen/ Jugendherbergen.	*a list of campsites/ youth hostels.*
einen Stadtplan.	*a map of the town.*

Was kann man machen? / *What can you do?*

Man kann/Wir können …	*You/We can …*
einen Einkaufsbummel machen.	*go on a shopping expedition.*
das Filmmuseum besuchen.	*visit the Film Museum.*
den Rheinturm besichtigen.	*visit the Rhine Tower.*
eine Stadtrundfahrt machen.	*do a tour of the town.*
in den Südpark gehen.	*go to the South Park.*

Zwei Fahrkarten, bitte! / *Two tickets, please!*

Wie komme ich am besten …	*What's the best way …*
zum Bahnhof?	*to the railway station?*
zur nächsten U-Bahn-Station?	*to the nearest underground station?*
zum Kino?	*to the cinema?*
Wo ist die nächste …	*Where's the nearest …*
Bushaltestelle?	*bus stop?*
S-Bahn-Station?	*S-Bahn station?*
Geh/Gehen Sie …	*Go …*
Nimm/Nehmen Sie …	*Take …*
links/rechts/geradeaus	*left/right/straight on*
die erste Straße rechts	*the first road on the right*
die zweite Straße links	*the second road on the left*
über die Brücke	*over the bridge*
an der Ampel/Kreuzung	*at the traffic lights/crossroads*

Ich möchte zwei Fahrkarten nach …, bitte.	*I'd like two tickets to …, please.*
Einfach oder hin und zurück?	*One-way or return?*
Erster oder zweiter Klasse?	*First or second class?*
Was kosten die Fahrkarten?	*How much are the tickets?*
Eine Fahrkarte kostet … Euro.	*One ticket costs … euros.*
Fährt der Zug direkt?	*Is this a direct train?*
Nein, Sie müssen in … umsteigen.	*No, you have to change in …*
Wann fährt der Zug ab?	*When does the train leave?*
Und wann kommt er an?	*When does it arrive?*
Die Fahrt wird … Minuten dauern.	*The journey will take … minutes.*

Wieder zu Hause! / *Home again!*

das Hemd	*shirt*
die Jacke	*jacket*
der Kapuzenpullover	*hooded jumper*
der Pullover	*jumper*
die Schuhe	*shoes*

unter dem Bett	*under the bed*
neben dem Computer	*next to the computer*
auf dem Regal	*on the shelf*
zwischen dem Bett und dem Stuhl	*between the bed and the chair*
vor dem Schreibtisch	*in front of the desk*
an der Tür	*on the door*
im Schrank	*in the wardrobe*
hinter dem Bett	*behind the bed*

Wir sind …	*We …*
gefahren/gegangen/ angekommen/ geschwommen.	*travelled/went/arrived/ swam …*
Wir haben …	*We …*
besichtigt/besucht.	*visited …*
gekauft/gespielt.	*bought/played …*
gesehen/gemacht.	*saw/did …*
getanzt.	*danced.*
gegessen/getrunken.	*ate/drank …*

Checklist

How well do you think you can do the following?			
Write a sentence for each one if you can.			
	I can do this well	I can do this but not very well	I can't do this yet
1. plan a trip and write a formal letter			
2. say what there is to see and do in a town			
3. ask for directions and buy train tickets			
4. say where things are in a room			
5. describe a trip using past tenses			
6. identify different styles of writing			

4A.1 Meine Gegend

1 **Find the words and fill them in. What Is the mystery word (in the tinted boxes down)?**

1 coast
2 large city
3 port in northern Germany
4 village
5 small town
6 in the mountains = *in den …*
7 country
8 Germany's capital
9 town

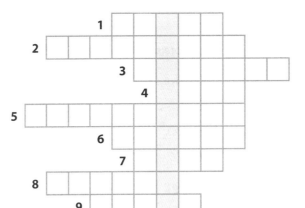

Mystery word: _____

2 🎧 **Listen to the six speakers and complete the sentences.**

1 This person lives in the ____mountains____ . She can _____ and _____ .

2 This one doesn't like living in the _____ because it is _____ .

3 He lives in _____ and thinks it's _____ because _____ .

4 He doesn't like living in _____ because _____ .

5 She thinks living in a _____ is _____ because _____ and _____ .

6 This person lives on the _____ . The problem is _____ .

4A.2 Bus und Bahn

1 Unjumble the words for forms of transport. Write the words in the boxes. Then draw lines to link the boxes to the correct pictures.

ARAFHRD

GUZ

SUB

RßATSNEHNAB

ADOOMTRR

ZULGFUEG

OTUA

2 Circle the correct article.

a Wir fahren mit (der) / dem U-Bahn in die Stadt.

b Ich fahre mit der / dem Bus zur Schule.

c Papa fährt mit der / dem Auto in den Urlaub.

d Man fährt mit der / dem Straßenbahn zum Krankenhaus.

e Wir fliegen mit der / dem Flugzeug nach New York.

f Die Hells Angels fahren mit der / dem Motorrad.

masculine	feminine	neuter
Bus	U-Bahn	Auto
	Straßenbahn	Flugzeug
		Motorrad

3 Use the expressions in the box to write three sentences saying <u>where</u> you go, <u>when</u> and <u>by what means of transport</u>. Remember the correct order in German: time, manner, place.

_____

_____

_____

Ich fahre	am Montag	mit dem Rad	in die Stadt.
	jeden Tag	mit dem Auto	zur Schule.
	am Wochenende	mit der Bahn	nach Hannover.

Umfrage: Bist du umweltfreundlich?

1 Find out how much your classmates care about the environment.
First, unjumble these questions.

1 zu du Gehst oft Fuß ? _____

2 Müll Trennst den du ? _____

3 du Container zum die Bringst Glasflaschen ? _____

4 Plastiktüten du Benutzt ? _____

5 du oder Duschst du badest ? _____

6 Strom du Sparst ? _____

2 Ask at least ten people in your class questions 1–6 from Activity 1
in German. Tick *Ja* or *Nein* to record their answers in the grid.

Question	Ja	Nein
1		
2		
3		
4		
5		
6		

3 Fill the gaps in this summary of your survey results.
(Watch out – the actions are listed in a different order.)

_____ people separate their rubbish.

_____ people take showers rather than baths.

_____ people save electricity.

_____ people go to the bottle bank.

_____ people don't use plastic bags.

_____ people often walk.

4 🎧 Listen: is each person eco-friendly or not? Tick *umweltfreundlich* or
umweltfeindlich.

1 umweltfreundlich ☐   umweltfeindlich ☐

2 umweltfreundlich ☐   umweltfeindlich ☐

3 umweltfreundlich ☐   umweltfeindlich ☐

4 umweltfreundlich ☐   umweltfeindlich ☐

5 umweltfreundlich ☐   umweltfeindlich ☐

1 *Umweltquiz.* **Find ten words about the environment in this grid. They can be down, across or diagonal.**

O	A	K	R	A	U	M	W	E	L	T	P
I	Z	P	U	E	Z	N	N	N	I	M	U
N	H	O	K	Ö	J	Ü	E	T	F	Ü	M
D	ß	L	N	W	T	I	P	W	W	L	V
U	M	Ü	A	L	G	E	R	A	T	L	E
S	Ü	S	T	R	O	G	R	L	D	B	R
T	L	Ä	E	F	Ä	C	Z	D	A	E	K
R	T	N	A	T	U	R	H	U	Ü	R	E
I	E	G	S	T	R	O	M	N	J	G	H
E	X	K	L	I	M	A	Z	G	O	Z	R

Ozonloch	Klima
Müllberg	Strom
Energie	Industrie
Umwelt	Entwaldung
Verkehr	Natur

2 **Read the sentences and write the German adjectives and their comparative and superlative forms into the gaps.**

schlimmer
gut
größte
am schlimmsten
größeres
am besten
besser
großes
schlimm

a Die Müllberge sind _____schlimm_____ (*bad*), der Verkehr ist _____ (*worse*), aber das Ozonloch ist _____ (*worst*).

b Duschen ist _____ (*good*), zu Fuß gehen ist _____ (*better*), aber Recycling ist _____ (*best*).

c Die Luftverschmutzung ist ein _____ (*big*) Problem, der Atommüll ist ein _____ (*bigger*) Problem, aber das _____ (*biggest*) Problem ist der Klimawandel.

3 **Which of these words are made up of two or more words put together? When you have found them, split them into their components and try to work out what they mean.**

a Treibhauseffekt _____

b Müllberg _____

c Natur _____

d Pflanze _____

e Ozonloch _____

f Wald _____

g Verkehr _____

h Klimawandel _____

1 🎧 **Listen to a conversation between grandfather and grandson. Are the statements below true (T), false (F) or not mentioned (NM)?**

a Peter enjoyed his first day at school. _____T_____

b His school has solar panels. _____

c His grandfather's school used to be nice and warm. _____

d Peter's school has four types of recycling bin. _____

e His grandfather was allowed to smoke at school. _____

f Peter's school has energy-saving computers. _____

g There are vegetables in the school's garden. _____

h Things were better in the old days. _____

2 **Read these sentences and decide whether they refer to past, present or future.**

a Alles war schmutzig. _____past_____

b Schulen werden umweltfreundlich sein. _____

c Wir haben vier Müllcontainer. _____

d Wir hatten keine Pflanzen. _____

e Unsere Schule ist sehr sauber. _____

f Wir werden energiesparende Computer haben. _____

1 Choose the most logical ends to these sentences.

1 Es ist schön ruhig,
2 Ich bin umweltfreundlich,
3 Hier ist es stressig,
4 Die Luft ist schlecht,
5 Ich musste eine Plastiktüte kaufen,
6 Ich gehe zu Fuß in die Stadt,

a weil es laut ist.
b weil wir auf dem Dorf leben.
c weil ich immer recycle.
d weil es gesund ist.
e weil es so viel Verkehr gibt.
f weil ich meine Stofftasche vergessen habe.

weil

The word *weil* ('because') has a comma before it and sends the verb to the end.

The dative

After prepositions like *mit* and *zu*, the dative form is used (m: *dem*, f: *der*, n: *dem*). *Zu der* is usually shortened to *zur* and *zu dem* to *zum*.

2 Write in *der* or *dem*.

a Ich fahre oft mit ___dem___ Rad.

b Wir fahren nie mit _____ Auto.

c Fährst du mit _____ Straßenbahn?

d Opa fährt mit _____ U-Bahn.

e Oma fährt mit _____ Bus.

These three use a shortened form:

f Wie komme ich _____ Krankenhaus?

g Ich fahre _____ Arbeit.

h Wir gehen _____ Bäckerei.

masculine	feminine	neuter
Bus	U-Bahn	Rad
	Arbeit	Auto
	Bäckerei	Krankenhaus
	Straßenbahn	

Comparative and superlative

For the comparative, add -er to the adjective:
toll ⟶ toll**er** (great, greater)   schlecht ⟶ schlecht**er** (bad, worse)

For some short adjectives, add an umlaut to the first vowel:
alt ⟶ **ält**er (old, older)

Some comparatives are irregular and have a different word altogether:
gut ⟶ besser (good, better)

For the superlative of regular adjectives, add *am* before the adjective and -*sten* or -*esten* to the end:
schlimm ⟶ **am** schlimm**sten** (bad, worst)

3 Fill in the comparative and superlative adjectives.

a Eine Kuh ist ___größer___ als eine Maus, aber ein Elefant ist am
_____ . (groß)

b Ein Audi ist _____ als ein VW, aber ein Mercedes ist am
_____ . (teuer)

c Reggae ist _____ als klassische Musik, aber Heavy Metal ist am
_____ . (laut)

Checking your written work

1 **Translate these simple sentences, keeping the spelling tips in mind.**

a My dog runs fast. _____

b I have a nice bike. _____

c We write a lot of letters. _____

d How many sausages have you eaten? _____

e I would like to go home. _____

f How far is Munich? _____

Tenses
If it's present tense, remember it may be an irregular verb.
If it's perfect tense, use *haben* or *sein* plus the past participle at the end.
If it's future tense, use *werden* plus the infinitive at the end.

2 **Find the German and English sentences that fit together.**

1	He travels by car.	_h_	**a**	Rauchst du?
2	He travelled by car.	_____	**b**	Er wird mit dem Auto fahren.
3	He will travel by car.	_____	**c**	Wir haben Plastiktüten benutzt.
4	We use plastic bags.	_____	**d**	Wir benutzen Plastiktüten.
5	We used plastic bags.	_____	**e**	Hast du geraucht?
6	We will use plastic bags.	_____	**f**	Er fährt mit dem Auto.
7	Do you smoke?	_____	**g**	Wirst du rauchen?
8	Did you smoke?	_____	**h**	Er ist mit dem Auto gefahren.
9	Will you smoke?	_____	**i**	Wir werden Plastiktüten benutzen.

3 **Write out these sentences with the words in the right order.**

a Wir werden / mit dem Bus / fahren / nach Bonn / am Freitag

_____

b Ich wohne / auf dem Land / mit meiner Mutter

_____

c Leo arbeitet / bei Radio Zoom / seit sechs Monaten / mit seinen Freunden

_____

Word order
Check that you have followed the rules: verb second, then time, manner, place.

Meine Gegend	My area
Ich wohne …	I live …
in einem Dorf	in a village
in einer Stadt/Großstadt	in a town/city
in einer Industriestadt	in an industrial town
in einer Kleinstadt	in a small town
am Stadtrand	in the suburbs
an der Küste	by the coast
auf dem Land	in the country
in den Bergen	in the mountains
Ich wohne (nicht) gern hier, weil …	I (don't) like living here because …
es viel Kriminalität gibt.	there's a lot of crime.
es zu viele Autos gibt.	there are too many cars.
es nichts für Jugendliche gibt.	there's nothing for young people.
man viel machen kann.	you can do lots, there's lots to do.
es … ist.	it's …
langweilig	boring
laut	noisy
praktisch	practical
ruhig	quiet
sauber	clean
schmutzig	dirty
schön	nice, beautiful
sicher	safe

Bus und Bahn	By bus and rail
Ich fahre mit …	I go/travel by …
dem Auto/Bus/Zug.	car/bus/train.
dem Fahrrad/Motorrad.	bike/motorbike.
der U-Bahn/Straßenbahn.	underground/tram.
Ich fliege mit dem Flugzeug.	I fly by plane.
Ich gehe zu Fuß.	I walk/go on foot.
zum Flughafen	to the airport
zur Schule/Arbeit	to school/work
zum Kino	to the cinema
nach Frankreich	to France
in den Urlaub	on holiday

Umweltschutz	Protecting the environment
Ich spare Strom.	I save energy.
Ich nehme keine Plastiktüten, sondern Stofftaschen.	I don't take plastic bags, I take cloth bags.
Meine Familie nutzt …	My family uses …
alternative Energien.	alternative energy.
Sonnen-/Windenergie.	solar/wind energy.
Ich dusche/Ich bade nicht.	I shower/I don't have a bath.
Wir haben drei Mülleimer.	We have three bins.
Wir trennen unseren Müll.	We separate our litter.
Ich recycle Papier/Dosen.	I recycle paper/cans.
Ich bringe Glasflaschen zum Container.	I take glass bottles to the bottle bank.
Ich habe …	I …
gebadet/geduscht.	bathed/showered.
… gebracht/genommen.	brought/took …
… genutzt/gespart.	used/saved …
… getrennt/recycelt.	separated/recycled …
Ich bin … gegangen/gefahren.	I went/travelled …
Ich werde …	I will …
baden/duschen.	bathe/shower.
… bringen/nehmen.	bring/take …
… nutzen/sparen.	use/save …
… trennen/recyceln.	separate/recycle …
… gehen/fahren.	go/travel …

Fünf vor zwölf	Five to twelve
der Atommüll	nuclear waste
das Aussterben von Tieren	extinction of animals
die Entwaldung	deforestation
der Klimawandel	climate change
die Luftverschmutzung	air pollution
die Müllberge	rubbish mountains
das Ozonloch	hole in the ozone layer
der Treibhauseffekt	greenhouse effect
viel Verkehr	a lot of traffic
Man muss …	We must …
mehr zu Fuß gehen.	walk more.

Checklist

How well do you think you can do the following? Write a sentence for each one if you can.	I can do this well	I can do this but not very well	I can't do this yet
1. describe where I live and give my opinion of it			
2. talk about ways to travel			
3. talk about ways to be environmentally friendly			
4. talk about environmental problems and solutions			
5. use linking word weil			
6. use the comparative and the superlative			

1 **Draw lines to link the matching sentence parts.**

1	Ich führe	**a**	Autos.
2	Ich helfe	**b**	im Garten.
3	Ich gebe	**c**	Babysitting.
4	Ich wasche	**d**	zu Hause.
5	Ich arbeite	**e**	Zeitungen aus.
6	Ich mache	**f**	Nachhilfeunterricht.
7	Ich trage	**g**	Hunde aus.

2 🎧 **Listen and fill in the details: job, opinion, money.**

1 Sven works in _____*a shop*_____ . It's _____ and

he earns _____ .

2 Anja earns money by _____ . She thinks it's

_____ but she gets _____ .

3 Martin works in _____ . The work is

_____ but he earns _____ .

4 Arno thinks his job is _____ . He delivers

_____ and earns _____ .

5 Susanne earns money by _____ . She earns

_____ but it's quite _____ .

3 🎧 **Listen again and note down, in English, one extra piece of information for each person.**

1 _____

2 _____

3 _____

4 _____

5 _____

4B.2 Meine Schule

1 *Richtig oder falsch?* For each sentence, circle *R* if it is *richtig* and *F* if it is *falsch*.

> To revise what you have learnt about German schools, see page 135 of your Student Book.

a In Großbritannien beginnt der Unterricht um acht Uhr. R / F

b In Deutschland geht man oft um 13 Uhr nach Hause. R / F

c In Deutschland kann man sitzen bleiben. R / F

d In Großbritannien gehen Kinder mit vier Jahren zur Schule. R / F

e In Deutschland muss man eine Uniform tragen. R / F

f In Deutschland gehen Kinder mit sechs Jahren zur Schule. R / F

g In Großbritannien macht man Abitur. R / F

h Im Gymnasium macht man Gymnastik. R / F

2 🎧 **Listen to these people and choose the correct option each time.**

1 This boy is doing <u>the equivalent of A-levels</u> / <u>an apprenticeship</u>.

2 This girl is doing <u>the equivalent of A-levels</u> / <u>an apprenticeship</u>.

3 This boy goes to <u>a grammar school</u> / <u>a comprehensive school</u>.

4 This girl goes to <u>a grammar school</u> / <u>a comprehensive school</u>.

5 This boy goes to <u>a grammar school</u> / <u>university</u>.

6 This girl goes is doing the equivalent of <u>A-levels</u> / <u>GCSEs</u>.

3 **Read these sentences and put a tick if you agree with the opinion and a cross if you don't.**

a Der Unterricht beginnt um acht Uhr. Das ist super. ☐

b Man muss eine Uniform tragen. Das ist doof. ☐

c Man geht um ein Uhr nach Hause. Das ist zu früh. ☐

d Man kann sitzen bleiben. Das macht Spaß. ☐

e Die Kinder kommen mit vier Jahren zur Schule. Das ist zu jung. ☐

f Die Schüler essen in der Kantine. Das ist besser, als um elf Uhr ein Käsebrot zu essen. ☐

4B.3 Und nächstes Jahr?

1 *Schulfächerquiz.* **Solve the clues and write the German subject names into the grid. What is the mystery subject, in the tinted boxes?**

1 Animals and plants

2 Countries

3 Classical or pop

4 Spoken in the UK and America

5 Spoken in Germany and Austria

6 Computer studies

7 'Bonjour!'

8 A science, but not chemistry

9 Painting and drawing

10 Adding and subtracting

The mystery subject is: _____

2 **Read the email below and answer the questions in English.**

a Is Sonja in England? _____

b What is her favourite subject? _____

c Does she have to learn it? _____

d How long has she been learning it? _____

e What does she think about physics? _____

f What will she do instead? _____

g Why? (2 reasons) _____ _____

h What will she do eventually? _____

Hallo Kate!

Welche Fächer lernst du in deiner Schule in England? Mein Lieblingsfach ist Englisch. Bei uns in Deutschland ist das ein Pflichtfach. Ich lerne schon seit fünf Jahren Englisch.

Ich finde Physik nicht so toll. Ich finde dieses Fach langweilig und schwer. Ich werde Physik nach der elften Klasse aufgeben und stattdessen* Erdkunde machen. Dieses Jahr habe ich in Erdkunde sehr gute Noten bekommen und ich finde es sehr interessant, etwas über andere Länder zu lernen.

In zwei Jahren werde ich Abitur machen und dann werde ich hoffentlich an der Uni Geographie studieren. Bis bald,
Sonja

*stattdessen – *instead*

4B.4 Berufe

1 Decide whether these phrases are said by a male or female. Write M or F in the boxes.

a Ich bin Ärztin. F

b Ich bin Hausfrau. ☐

c Ich bin Briefträger. ☐

d Ich bin Polizistin. ☐

e Ich bin Krankenpflegerin. ☐

f Ich bin Lkw-Fahrer. ☐

g Ich bin Informatiker. ☐

h Ich bin Sekretärin. ☐

2 Write in the jobs that these people would like to do. Remember to adjust the word according to whether the person is male or female.

a Petra would like to work with children in a school:

Ich möchte _____ werden.

b Hans wants to stay at home and do housework:

Ich möchte _____ werden.

c Birgit would like to work in a hospital but not as a doctor:

Ich möchte _____ werden.

d Boris likes the idea of flying planes:

Ich möchte _____ werden.

e Iris wants to work in a shop:

Ich möchte _____ werden.

f Klaus would like to help ill people:

Ich möchte _____ werden.

g Claudia enjoys working with computers:

Ich möchte _____ werden.

Informatiker/in
Pilot/in
Lehrer/in
Krankenpfleger/in
Arzt/Ärztin
Verkäufer/in
Hausfrau/mann

4B.5 Mein Schultag

1 🎧 **Svenja is talking to her mother. Listen to the conversation and answer the questions in English.**

a What was school like today?

_____

b What two problems were there in the first lesson?

_____

c What was the problem in the second lesson?

_____

d What did Svenja think of the teacher?

_____

e What nearly happened?

_____

f What weren't they allowed to do in the maths lesson?

_____

g What was good about the day?

_____

h Why? Give details.

_____

2 **Remember that the verb always comes second in a German sentence. Rewrite these sentences using new beginnings as indicated.**

a Wir hatten Biologie in der ersten Stunde.

Heute _____ .

b Kinder kommen mit sechs Jahren in die Schule.

In der Schweiz _____ .

c Wir trinken Milch.

In der Pause _____ .

d Der Unterricht ist interessant.

In meiner Schule _____ .

e Wir werden auf das Gymnasium gehen.

Nächstes Jahr _____ .

f Ursel ist in die Grundschule gekommen.

Letztes Jahr _____ .

g Ich möchte Lehrerin werden.

Später _____ .

h Ich werde Hausaufgaben machen.

Am Wochenende _____ .

1 *für* + accusative
What is this person saving for? Write in *einen* (m), *eine* (f) or *ein* (n).

Ich spare für _____ein_____ Handy, _____ E-Gitarre,

_____ Computer, _____ Rad, _____

MP3-Player und _____ Uhr.

masculine	feminine	neuter
Computer	Gitarre	Handy
MP3-Player	Uhr	Rad

2 **Present, perfect and future**
This person has changed her habits. Put each present tense sentence into the perfect and then the future, using the details given in brackets at the end.

a *Present*: Normalerweise dusche ich um 6 Uhr.

   Perfect: Gestern _____habe ich um 7 Uhr geduscht._____ (um 7 Uhr)

   Future: Morgen _____werde ich um 8 Uhr duschen._____ (um 8 Uhr)

b *Present*: Normalerweise esse ich Cornflakes zum Frühstück.

   Perfect: Gestern _____ (Toast)

   Future: Morgen _____ (Joghurt)

c *Present*: Normalerweise fahre ich mit dem Bus zur Schule.

   Perfect: Gestern _____ (Auto)

   Future: Morgen _____ (Rad)

> Remember, many verbs use *haben* to form the perfect tense, but some – including *fahren* – use *sein* instead.

d *Present*: Normalerweise fahren wir in den Ferien nach Frankreich.

   Perfect: Letztes Jahr _____ (Spanien)

   Future: Nächstes Jahr _____ (Schweden)

e *Present*: Normalerweise spielen wir am Wochenende Fußball.

   Perfect: Letztes Wochenende _____ (Tennis)

   Future: Nächstes Wochenende _____ (Volleyball)

f *Present*: Normalerweise mache ich meine Hausaufgaben um 15 Uhr.

   Perfect: Gestern _____ (um 16 Uhr)

   Future: Morgen _____ (gar nicht!)

'Filler' words

1 Read the message and cross out all the 'filler' words.

Note that when you have taken out all the unnecessary words, it is still completely understandable. We do the same in English, often using words like 'well' and 'like'.

> Na, wie war denn die Party eigentlich? Also, ich fand sie ganz gut. Naja, die Musik war etwas altmodisch, aber das Essen war wirklich lecker.

Working out the meaning of unknown words

2 In German, words are put together to make new ones. Draw one line to match the German words to the English explanations and another line to the actual English meanings.

German	English explanation	English meaning
Gesamtschule	flying thing	postman
Nachhilfe	hour plan	nurse
Nebenjob	stay sitting	confectionery
Süßigkeit	letter carrier	comprehensive school
Fahrrad	earth studies	bike
Zeitschrift	sweetness	tuition
Stundenplan	school yard	magazine
Oberstufe	carer of the sick	aeroplane
sitzen bleiben	after help	repeat a school year
Schulhof	upper stage	geography
Erdkunde	time writing	timetable
Krankenpflegerin	whole school	sixth form
Briefträger	side job	playground
Flugzeug	driving wheel	part-time job

Ich habe einen Nebenjob	*I have a part-time job*
Ich trage Zeitungen aus.	*I deliver newspapers.*
Ich mache Babysitting.	*I do babysitting.*
Ich führe Hunde aus.	*I walk dogs.*
Ich arbeite in einem Geschäft.	*I work in a shop.*
Ich helfe im Garten.	*I do gardening.*
Ich wasche Autos.	*I wash cars.*
Ich gebe Nachhilfeunterricht.	*I give extra tuition.*
Ich helfe zu Hause.	*I help at home.*
Ich bekomme kein Taschengeld.	*I don't get any pocket money.*
Ich bekomme 8 Euro pro Stunde.	*I get 8 euros an hour.*
Ich arbeite, um … zu kaufen.	*I work to buy …*
Ich spare für …	*I'm saving up for …*
ein Fahrrad/ein Handy.	*a bike/ a mobile phone.*
Kleidung/Make-up.	*clothes/make-up.*

Meine Schule	*My school*
die Gesamtschule	*comprehensive school*
das Gymnasium	*grammar school*
die Hauptschule	*secondary school (to age 15)*
die Realschule	*secondary school (to age 16)*
die Grundschule	*primary school*
Ich besuche eine/die Gesamtschule.	*I go to a comprehensive school.*
Ich gehe auf ein/das Gymnasium.	*I go to a grammar school.*
Ich bin in der 10. Klasse.	*I'm in Year 11.*
Ich werde …	*I will …*
mein Abitur machen.	*do my A levels.*
eine Lehre machen.	*do an apprenticeship.*
auf die Oberstufe kommen.	*go into the sixth form.*
meinen Realschulabschluss machen.	*do my GCSEs.*
an der Universität studieren.	*study at university.*

Und nächstes Jahr?	*And next year?*
Biologie	*biology*
Chemie	*chemistry*
Chinesisch	*Chinese*
Deutsch	*German*
Englisch	*English*
Erdkunde	*geography*
Französisch	*French*
Geschichte	*history*
Informatik	*IT*
Kunst	*art*
Mathe	*maths*
Musik	*music*
Naturwissenschaften	*science*
Physik	*physics*
Religion	*religious education*

Spanisch	*Spanish*
Sport	*PE*
… ist mein Lieblingsfach.	*… is my favourite subject.*
Ich bekomme gute Noten.	*I get good grades.*
Ich habe … als Leistungskurs gewählt.	*I chose … as main/specialist subjects.*
Ich lerne seit zwei Jahren …	*I've been learning … for two years.*

Berufe	*Professions*
Ich möchte … werden.	*I'd like to be a …*
Arzt, Ärztin	*doctor*
Briefträger/in	*postman/woman*
Geschäftsmann, Geschäftsfrau	*businessman/woman*
Hausmann, Hausfrau	*house husband, housewife*
Informatiker/in	*IT specialist*
Kellner/in	*waiter, waitress*
Krankenpfleger/in	*nurse*
Lkw-Fahrer/in	*truck driver*
Modedesigner/in	*fashion designer*
Polizist/in	*policeman/woman*
Sekretär/in	*secretary*
Tierarzt, Tierärztin	*vet*
Verkäufer/in	*shop assistant*

Checklist

How well do you think you can do the following?			
Write a sentence for each one if you can.			
	I can do this well	**I can do this but not very well**	**I can't do this yet**
1. talk about part-time jobs, spending and saving			
2. talk about school life in Germany/UK			
3. talk about what I've done this year at school and what I'm going to do next year			
4. talk about different jobs and say what job I would like to do in the future			
5. use masculine and feminine forms of job words			
6. use *ich möchte … werden*			

Zoom Deutsch 2 Foundation Workbook CD Track listings

1   Copyright line

Pronunciation

2   Seite 4, Consonants/Konsonanten
3   Seite 4, *g*
4   Seite 4, *j*
5   Seite 4, *r*
6   Seite 4, *s*; *sp*, *st*
7   Seite 4, Übung 1
8   Seite 4, *ß*
9   Seite 5, *ss*
10   Seite 5, Übung 2
11   Seite 5, *v*
12   Seite 5, *w*
13   Seite 5, Übung 3
14   Seite 5, *z*
15   Seite 5, Combination of consonants *ch*
16   Seite 5, *ig*
17   Seite 5, *sch*
18   Seite 5, *pf*
19   Seite 5, *zw*
20   Seite 6, Vowels/Vokale long a/langes *a*
21   Seite 6, short a/ kurzes *a*
22   Seite 6, hat/ cat/ Handy
23   Seite 6, short e/ kurzes *e*
24   Seite 6, long e/ langes *e*
25   Seite 6, Übung 4
26   Seite 6, *i*
27   Seite 6, short o/kurzes *o*
28   Seite 6, long o/ langes *o*
29   Seite 6, Übung 5
30   Seite 7, *u*
31   Seite 7, long u/ langes *u*
32   Seite 7, Übung 6
33   Seite 7, Combination of vowels *ie*
34   Seite 7, *ei*
35   Seite 7, Übung 7
36   Seite 7, *au*
37   Seite 7, Umlauts *a ä*
38   Seite 7, *o ö*
39   Seite 7, *u ü*
40   Seite 7, Übung 8

Einheit 0: Hallo!

41   Seite 8, Übung 2
42   Seite 9, Übung 2
43   Seite 10, Übung 3
44   Seite 11, Übung 2
45   Seite 12, Übung 2

Einheit 1A: Mein Tag

46   Seite 17, Übung 2
47   Seite 18, Übung 1
48   Seite 19, Übung 1
49   Seite 22, Übung 1

Einheit 1B: Wir feiern!

50   Seite 25, Übung 2
51   Seite 27, Übung 1

Einheit 2A: Die Medien

52   Seite 35, Übung 1
53   Seite 36, Übung 2
54   Seite 38, Übung 1

Einheit 2B: Hobbys

55   Seite 40, Übung 3
56   Seite 42, Übung 3
57   Seite 43, Übung 1
58   Seite 46, Übung 1

Einheit 3A: Gesundes Leben

59   Seite 49, Übung 2
60   Seite 50, Übung 2
61   Seite 51, Übung 2

Einheit 3B: Ausflug nach Düsseldorf

62   Seite 57, Übung 1
63   Seite 58, Übung 1
64   Seite 61, Übung 1

Einheit 4A: Die Umwelt

65   Seite 64, Übung 2
66   Seite 66, Übung 4
67   Seite 68, Übung 1

Einheit 4B: Schule und Zukunft

68   Seite 72, Übungen 2 und 3
69   Seite 73, Übung 2
70   Seite 76, Übung 1